Time's Up on Timed Tests

How to Teach Math Facts for Understanding

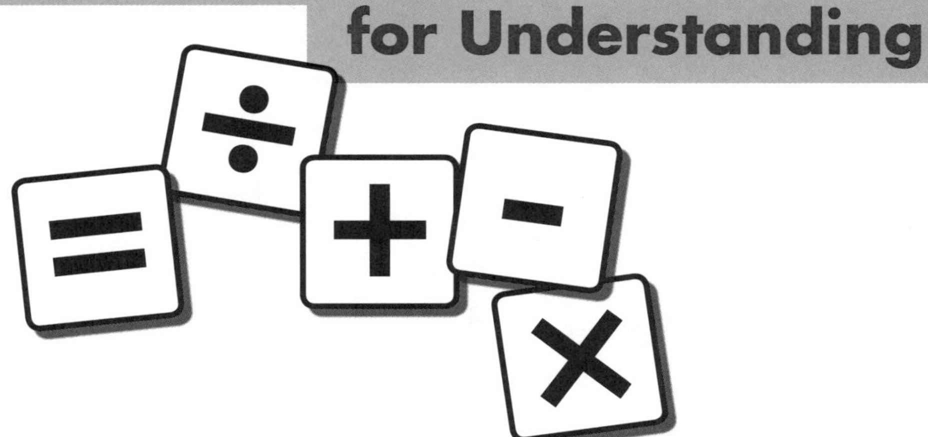

Kristin Hilty • Eliza Sorte-Thomas

Peterborough, New Hampshire

It was with a strong passion about this subject that drove both of us to write this book. We have watched many children suffer from anxiety and poor self-esteem due to results from timed tests. In fact, many students will refer to themselves as "stupid" because they can't reach an unrealistic goal.

We dedicate this book to all of the Joeys out there . . . our hope is that you never again feel you are not capable of success because you are not the fastest in the class. Always remember—speed alone doesn't win the race.

—Kristin and Eliza

Published by SDE Professional Development Resources
10 Sharon Road, PO Box 500
Peterborough, NH 03458
1-800-321-0401
www.SDE.com

ISBN: 978-1-63133-076-6

Book design: Eva Ruutopõld
Illustrations: Dana Regan

Printed in the United States of America
20 19 18 17 16 1 2 3 4 5

Table of Contents

Introduction

Background knowledge, or **schema**, is an essential component of reading comprehension, including, but not limited to, sight words and word-decoding strategies. Math is no different.

Math facts, and the strategies students need to retrieve them, are essential for problem-solving success. Without schema, math facts will remain isolated and unconnected. Too often, math facts are memorized and not understood; understood but not automatic; fast but not accurate; or some combination of all of the above. In response to state standard expectations, district and state assessments, and a teacher's knowledge that these facts are essential, teachers often resort to teaching the way they were instructed in math—by teaching their students to memorize facts and repeat them under pressure using anxiety-ridden timed tests.

Our goal in writing this book is to change the way we teach students the necessary mathematical underpinnings called math facts. We hope that we can provide you with the information and tools you'll need to feel empowered enough to call a time-out on timed tests and ultimately say, "Time's up!" on using them all together.

We will provide you with methods for teaching math facts that will lead your students to fluency. This fluency will not be in isolation, but rather in conjunction with the bigger picture of mathematical thinking and problem-solving. Instead of relying solely on memorization, students will learn how to use strategies to develop understanding. This understanding will lead to accuracy. Purposeful and meaningful practice, with an attention to precision, will then lead to increased automaticity and speed.

schema (n):

an organization of concepts and actions

Timed Tests—
Let's Make Them Things of the Past

This book has become a passion for us as teachers—a soapbox issue, if you will. We have seen the good, the bad, and the ugly in teaching students their math facts. Now it's time we did something about it. We believe this book will provide a launch pad that will help teachers create real change in the classroom, ultimately leading to real results.

A not-so-distant mathematical memory of ours inspires us to do better because now we know better. Without too much effort, we can both take ourselves back to a classroom in either small town Montana or suburban Ohio, filled with all of our friends and classmates. Even from opposite sides of the country, we share the same vivid memory. Perhaps it will sound familiar to you as well.

We walk into a room filled with rows of desks. On each desk we see a half-sized sheet of paper upside-down. We know what this means . . . a ***timed test****!*

Even as young students we understood that some students taking the test would be successful (they always were), and some would not do well at all (they never did). We knew that the fast would get faster, and the slower-working students would get even more disenfranchised. This understanding alone produced a sense of foreboding in many of us before the test even began.

The timer is set (a loud kitchen timer—no fancy SMART board or Internet timer for us). We barely sit down and we're told, "GO!" The noise of pencils scratching on paper is enough to distract the easiest of the distractible. Stress levels, which were already elevated at the idea of a timed test, are now skyrocketing. What seemed like only seconds later, we're told to stop. "PENCILS DOWN!" We're then instructed to pass our paper to the person behind us for grading.

There seemed to be only two possible scenarios: Those who always seemed to get all 100 items right were soon celebrating once again, or those who always struggled under the pressure of a timed test once again felt a dreaded and toxic mix of self-disappointment and humiliation. After grading, the scores were read out loud for the entire class to hear. To cap it all off, those perfectly scored tests were hung on a wall of fame, and those not making the grade were crumpled and thrown into the bin of shame.

timed test (n):

a short timing done repeatedly to measure speed of fact recall, typically used with addition and subtraction within 20 and/or multiplication and division of facts up to 12 x 12, or up to 144 divided by 12

As the class moved on to the daily content, no ideas were given for improvement, no strategies were shown, no patterns were pointed out. Occasionally, a sympathetic friend would show someone a calculation trick, but this "trick" taught no meaning, never helped when time was of the essence, and did no good for improvement. The next day in our classroom from the past, it was just like the movie ***Groundhog Day***, and we repeated the exact same routine and got the exact same results.

As the saying goes, "The definition of insanity is doing the same thing over and over again and expecting different results."

It's Time for Something New

Fast forward several years (about 20 for us authors), and many of the students from the past have grown up to become teachers. Incredibly, we see that for the most part, many teachers are still creating this anxiety-ridden, unproductive environment for our young (who are learning it for the first time) and older (who should have "gotten it" grade levels ago) mathematicians. There has to be a better way!

Our hope is that we can give you educators and your students the alternatives you've been looking for. We can remove the dreaded timed tests. We can skip the mind-numbing minute races. We can eliminate the tricks. We can reduce the anxiety. And we can build the background knowledge, or schema, students need with their math facts to develop true long-lasting number sense.

PART 1:
All about Fluency

PART 1:
All about Fluency

Fluency in Mathematics

Fluency. It's a loaded word in education right now. Many state standards allude to it, but they are hesitant to provide a real definition. In this book, we will address the concept head-on and give you a definition that you can believe in. Fluency does not, in our opinion, equate to just memorization. However, students who are fluent ***will*** memorize and be able to recall their facts as part of their fluency. The biggest difference between fluency AS memorization and fluency that LEADS TO memorization is that students who forget their math facts can still be fluent. It has been said that anything that is memorized can be forgotten. If that's true, then students could lose their fluency. But, we'll give you ways to ensure that even if your students haven't memorized their facts ***yet***, they can still be fluent, and they can still solve a problem because they will have multiple strategies and, therefore, multiple entry points for understanding. More importantly, they can find an answer when needed.

fluency (n):

the ability to solve a math fact with understanding; to solve with accuracy and efficiency

In this book, when we say ***fluency***, we are saying: fluency = understanding (including flexibility) + accuracy (attention to precision) + efficiency (strategy, memory, and reasonableness of time). So, if students can solve their multiplication facts through 100 fluently, they ***understand*** them, they get them ***correct***, and they do them in a ***reasonable, productive, efficient time frame***.

understanding
+ accuracy
+ efficiency

fluency

In her book ***Number Talks***, Sherri Parrish says that fluency is "knowing how a number can be **composed** and **decomposed** and using that information to be flexible and efficient with solving problems."

compose (v):

to put a number's parts back together; for example, the number 432 can be composed of 400, 30, and 2, or 200, 200, and 32.

Math educators have learned a lot about fluency from our friends in reading. Reading teachers learned that it wasn't enough to develop speedy readers. They saw students who could read as fast as a racing locomotive, but they had little understanding of what they had read. Their comprehension cars were empty. Clearly speed was one component of fluency, but it's not the only one. Fluency with math facts follows a similar track. We don't want our mathematical thinkers to jump the rails and be super-fast and have no idea what those numbers mean or how they work.

decompose (v):

to break a number into parts; for example, the number 346 can be broken into 3 hundreds, 4 tens, and 6 ones, or 1 hundred, 1 hundred, 1 hundred, and 46 ones

The Fear Factor

Math anxiety as a result of timed tests has been documented and, according to the work of Gerardo Ramirez and colleagues, has appeared in research in students as young as five. This situation presents a very pressing challenge: How can teachers create mathematical thinkers when their pupils are ridden with anxiety?

Well, here is our answer to the above-stated question: In order to develop mathematical thinkers, we are going to hold students accountable for doing their addition/subtraction and multiplication/division facts fluently. But when we say ***fluently***, we mean ***with understanding***, ***with accuracy***, and ***with efficiency***. Speed, as you'll notice, isn't in the definition. And we know we can help our students reach this goal without the use of the dreaded timed tests.

Another leader who is making it her mission to create an educational system that teaches fluency without fear is Dr. Jo Boaler from Stanford University. Boaler says:

> *"Mathematics facts are important, but the memorization of math facts through times table repetition, practice, and timed testing is unnecessary and damaging."*

Dr. Boaler also says, "The best way to develop fluency with numbers is to develop number sense and to work with numbers in different ways, not to blindly memorize without number sense." We could not agree more.

Apparently, we aren't the only ones who agree. A favorite educational leader of ours is Marilyn Burns. She's been influencing math instruction for decades, and her approach has resonated with teachers and is successful for students. In her classic book, ***About Teaching Mathematics: A K–8 Resource Guide***, Burns states:

> *"Memorization has an important role in computation. Calculating mentally and with paper and pencil requires having basic number facts committed to memory. However, memorization should follow, not lead, instruction that builds children's understanding. The emphasis in mathematics must always be on thinking, reasoning, and making sense."*

And it's not only math leaders who say this. In the 1970s, Fortune 500 business leaders valued skills such as computation (which uses math facts). In fact, computation was the second most important skill, while problem-solving fell in at number 12. In 1999, however, the list had changed, and computation had moved to second from the bottom versus second from the top. (See the chart on the next page.) Even though we're years past 1999, with continuously changing technologies, we need thinkers in the workforce, not rote memorizers. If we teach students to be fluent based on the way we've described fluency, students will be flexible thinkers (aka, problem-solvers); they'll still be able to do computation; and memorization will happen. These skills go hand-in-hand when built from understanding.

However, if we continue to place speed at the top of our list when teaching math facts, will we get the desired results—the results that will truly set our students up for success both in school and when they go out into the real world and find a job? Will our students see themselves as mathematical thinkers? Will they be truly proficient with their math facts? Has it worked for us so far? We're hoping you're shaking your head ***no*** to those questions. We have one final question for you: Isn't it time to take the time to teach math right? We're really hoping you are nodding ***yes*** now!

Fortune 500 most valued skills in **1970**	
1	Writing
2	Computational Skills
3	Reading Skills
4	Oral Communications
5	Listening Skills
6	Personal Career Development
7	Creative Thinking
8	Leadership
9	Goal-Setting/Motivation
10	Teamwork
11	Organizational Effectiveness
12	Problem-Solving
13	Interpersonal Skills

Fortune 500 most valued skills in **1999**	
1	Teamwork
2	Problem-Solving
3	Interpersonal Skills
4	Oral Communications
5	Listening Skills
6	Personal Career Development
7	Creative Thinking
8	Leadership
9	Goal-Setting/Motivation
10	Writing
11	Organizational Effectiveness
12	Computational Effectiveness
13	Reading Skills

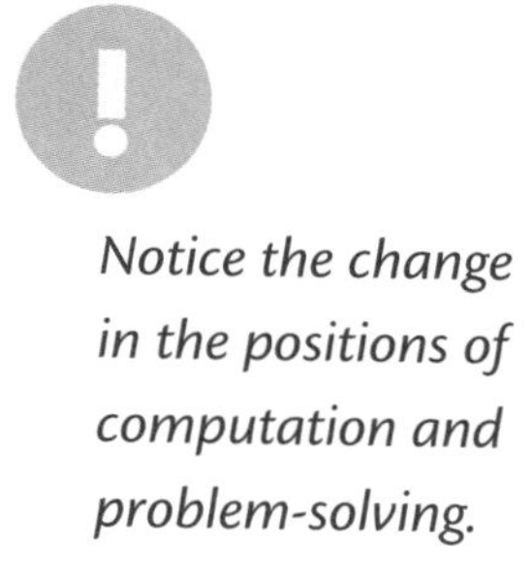

Notice the change in the positions of computation and problem-solving.

Fluency Expectations

Fluency has taken on a life of its own in many classrooms, districts, and states. However, fluency is really a means to an end—a skill set teachers want students to have and to develop. In many standards, the language used (or not used) confuses the issue. Standards may say, "students will fluently . . ." but then fail to explain what is meant by the word ***fluently***. Teachers are left on their own to decide what that really means.

It's important for us to remember to think about fluency as something that will aid students with subsequent skills. It's something we want to foster and develop, not something we want to check off of a list so we can say, "Yep, this student is fluent," or "No, this student can't fluently add." Fluency expectations extend beyond basic facts. They can be pivotal in future success both emotionally and academically.

In many states today, as per the Common Core or standards similar to the Common Core, the expectation is that, by the end of second grade, students will know their addition and subtraction facts to 20 from memory, and by the end of third grade, students will know their multiplication and division facts through 100 from memory. This is where our focus will be for this book.

(See the next page for an example of one state's mathematics standards.)

It's important as we move forward to note that there is no time expectation (either explicit or implicit) included in the definition of ***fluency*** or ***from memory***. This is an expectation that has been placed on our students, ourselves, and our systems—an expectation to which we should find alternatives. Educators MUST say, "Time's up on timed tests," and focus on mathematical proficiency so students can be successful down the long, arduous, exciting, and incredibly important road of mathematics learning.

Grade Level	Strategies and/or Equations and Standard Algorithms Where are the Math Facts *from memory*?
K	**K.OA.1** Represent addition and subtraction with objects, fingers, mental images, drawings, sounds, acting out, verbal explanations, expressions, and equations. **"Kindergarten students should see addition and subtraction equations, and student writing of equations in Kindergarten is encouraged, but it is not required."** **K.OA.3** Decompose numbers less than or equal to 10 into pairs in more than one way by using objects or drawings, and record each decomposition by a drawing or **equation**. **K.OA.4** For any number from 1 to 9, find the number that makes 10 when added to the given number by using objects or drawings, and record the answer with a drawing or **equation**. **K.OA.5** Fluently add and subtract w/in 5.
1	**1.NBT.4** Add w/in 100: including understanding sometimes it is necessary to compose a 10 in the ones place (regroup). **1.NBT.5** Given a two-digit number, mentally find 10 more or 10 less than, without having to count, explain reasoning. **1.NBT.6** Subtract multiples of 10 in the range from 10–90 (positive or zero differences), using concrete models or drawings and strategies based on place value, properties of operations, and/or the relationship between addition and subtraction; relate the strategy to a **written method** and explain the reasoning being used. **1.OA.3** Apply properties of operations as strategies to add and subtract (students need not use formal terms). **1.OA.6** Fluently add and subtract w/in 10. **1.OA.7** Understand the meaning of the equal sign, and determine if **equations** involving addition and subtraction are true or false. **1.OA.8** Determine the unknown whole number in an **addition or subtraction equation** to three whole numbers.
2	**2.OA.2** Fluently add and subtract w/in 20 using mental strategies (such as counting on, making 10, decomposing a number leading to a 10, using relationship between addition and subtraction, creating easier or known sums, creating known equivalent). **2.OA.3** Determine whether a group of objects (up to 20) has an odd or even number of members (by pairing objects or counting them by 2s). Write an **equation** to express an even number as a sum or two equal addends. **2.OA.4** Use addition to find the total number of objects arranged in rectangular arrays with up to five rows and up to five columns; write an **equation** to express the total as a sum of equal addends. **2.NBT.5** Fluently add and subtract w/in 100 using strategies based on place value, properties of operations, and/or relationship between addition and subtraction. **2.NBT.6** Add up to four two-digit numbers using strategies based on place value and properties of operations. **2.NBT.7** Add and subtract w/in 1000 (using concrete models or drawings and strategies based on place value, properties of operations and/or relationship between addition and subtraction) including understand of hundreds, tens, and ones, and compose/decompose tens and hundreds. **2.NBT.8** Mentally add 10 or 100 to a given number 100–900, and mentally subtract 10 or 100 from a given number 100–900. ***By end of Grade 2, know *from memory* all sums of two one-digit numbers.**
3	**3.OA.7** Fluently multiply and divide w/in 100. **3.NBT.2** Fluently add and subtract w/in 1000 using strategies and **algorithms** based on place value, properties of operations, and/or the relationship between addition and subtraction. **3.NBT.3** Multiply one-digit whole numbers by multiples of 10 in the range 10–90 (e.g., 9 x 80, 5 x 60) using strategies based on place value and properties of operations. ***By the end of Grade 3, know *from memory* all products of two one-digit numbers.**
4	**4.NBT.4** Fluently add and subtract multi-digit whole numbers using the **standard algorithm.** **4.NBT.5** Multiply a whole number of up to four digits by a one-digit whole number, and multiply two two-digit numbers, using strategies based on place value and properties of operations. Illustrate and explain the calculations using **equations,** rectangular arrays, and/or area models. **4.NBT.6** Find whole-number quotients and remainders with up to four-digit dividends and one-digit divisors, using strategies based on place value, the properties of operations, and/or the relationship between multiplication and division. Illustrate and explain the calculation by using **equations**, rectangular arrays, and/or area models.
5	**5.NBT.5** Fluently multiply multi-digit whole numbers using the **standard algorithm.** **5.NBT.6** Find whole-number quotients of whole numbers with up to four-digit dividends and two-digit divisors, using strategies based on place value, the properties of operations, and/or the relationship between multiplication and division. Illustrate and explain the calculation by using **equations**, rectangular arrays, and/or area models. **5.NBT.7** Add, subtract, multiply, and divide decimals to hundredths, using concrete materials, drawings, and strategies based on place value, the properties of operations, and/or the relationship between addition and subtraction; relate the strategy to a written method and explain the reasoning used.
6	**6.NS.2** Fluently divide multi-digit numbers using the **standard algorithm**. **6.NS.3** Fluently add, subtract, multiply, and divide multi-digit decimals using the **standard algorithm** for each operation.

- **Solving word problems is the application of these skills and appears in all grade levels of this document.**
- **Fluency = understanding + accuracy + efficiency**

PART 2: All about Addition and Subtraction

PART 2: All about Addition and Subtraction

Teaching for Understanding

Teaching addition and subtraction is a bit different from teaching multiplication and division, and yet, educators still often attempt to teach the operations of addition and subtraction using the same strategies, including the same unsuccessful strategy—timed tests. We'd like to introduce a different approach to teaching these operations, an approach we think you will find more successful, and your students will find more engaging. But before we dive in, let's take a moment to explore addition and subtraction and how they are deeply connected to each other.

inverse relationship (n):

when two operations are related and work together; in addition, parts are put together to make a whole, such as 3 + 5 = 8; in subtraction, parts are taken away from the whole, such as 8 – 5 = 3; the inverse relationship arises because of the balance between the operations on either side of the equal sign

We want students to see that there's a relationship between the numbers in a mathematical sentence. They must also realize that when they see the equal sign, it is not indicative of an answer immediately following. So often, students only see the equal sign on the right side of the equation, which gives them this false understanding that an answer must follow it. As teachers, we need to mix things up and place the equal sign on both sides of the equation to help students understand that this symbol signifies a relationship between the numbers on both sides of the equation.

Another relationship students need to know and be able to apply is the **inverse relationship** between addition and subtraction. This relationship is at the center of understanding addition and subtraction. As the understanding of the relationship between the operations strengthens, it becomes more natural, more automatic. Students can use their knowledge or comfort with one operation to help them understand the other. Therefore students become more fluent with their addition and subtraction facts. When we teach addition and subtraction, we want students to understand the part-part-whole connection.

A New Approach

First, as teachers, we want to begin all new concepts with **concrete** instruction. This should be our "go-to" regardless of the mathematical content. Introducing any and all new concepts with concrete instruction should be the way we do business. Next, we also want to provide multiple and varied exposures to a variety of tasks and experiences. This means letting go of the idea that once an idea is taught, we are done with it and can move on. Finally, we want to connect the teaching to students' background knowledge and their everyday lives so they can relate to what they're learning.

concrete (adj):

using hands-on manipulatives to deliver math instruction conceptually (i.e., teddy bear counters, base-10 blocks, bean sticks, etc.)

A word of caution is in order here: It is during this instruction that educators often want to move quickly; we feel the pressure of content and the stress of the vast amount of "stuff" that students are going to need to learn during the year. We may also feel pressure from the school, from parents, from colleagues, or even from our past teaching experience. However, this is also a time when we can win a big victory by choosing to act purposefully to **Move slow now, so we can move fast later.** What we mean by that is this: Move slowly during instruction and practice, as this will enable students to master their skills and later move quickly as they work. Another bonus from taking this approach is that we will not need to go back and reteach as often or for as long if we do it right the first time.

story of a number (n):

all of the ways a number can be considered and examined

The Story of a Number

So . . . where do we start? Begin by looking at numbers as a whole and combinations of numbers as their parts. We ask our students to think about:

- What is that number (concretely)?
- How can that number be composed and decomposed?
- What does the number look like with manipulatives when broken apart into its pieces, and then conversely put back together into its whole form?

In answering these questions, students learn the **story of a number**.

Helpful Hint! *Lead students through the numbers 1 through 10. Give them the concrete experience of moving, making, and manipulating the numbers. Once numbers 1 through 10 are fully understood, help students see the numbers beyond 10 as "10 and some more."*

To help students understand the idea of a number story, explain that it is kind of like a story they would read. There are characters, patterns, similarities, and differences. Point out that in learning a number story, they will discover the combinations that make up a number. Remind them to look for similarities and differences, as well as patterns. Tell them to be on the lookout for the "characters" or numbers that appear over and over again.

For each number being explored, create an anchor chart that shows how the number can be broken apart. A great way to do this is to have students gather on the carpet or around a table with their whiteboards and their manipulatives. Let's use 5 as an example. As stated earlier, you'll want to begin instruction with concrete materials, so be sure to pass out 5 manipulatives to each student. Ask students to work with the manipulatives to discover all of the possible combinations used to make 5. You can easily formatively assess their understanding as they explore, and redirect them as necessary. Allow students opportunities to talk things through with each other. As they work, record the combinations they discover on the anchor chart.

When students return to their seats they should record their representations in a journal. Allow them to show what they know, and don't be upset if they seem to be simply copying what was recorded in the class chart. They're just showing their understanding. It can be hard to not hand out something for them to fill in, but fight that urge and allow them to represent their thinking in their own way. You can provide support for them when needed, of course, but when possible, let them have opportunities to construct meaning and organization. In this exploration you're the guide. Ask open-ended questions such as:

- What do you see?
- What do you notice?
- How might you arrange them?
- How can you show me?

Story of 5

0 and 5 make 5
1 and 4 make 5
2 and 3 make 5
3 and 2 make 5
4 and 1 make 5
5 and 0 make 5

Helpful Hint! *Determine which numbers you'll be covering with students and create an addition journal for students to explore, record, and make sense of composing and decomposing numbers. A pre-created journal could be especially helpful for a large class, for students who struggle with organization, or for you as you begin a new journey into different methods for instruction of fluency. In the Reproducibles section, we have provided some templates for this addition journal.*

These templates are open-ended enough to allow your students to think and not just fill in. Or they can be used as models for them to create their own.

Number Bracelets

Let's move forward in time a bit. You have guided students through the stories of each number 1 through 10. You've spent time concretely, pictorially, and abstractly learning about the numbers and their part-part-whole relationship. You've done this in order 1, 2, 3, . . . 10, you've done this as a whole class, with partners, with different types of manipulatives. You've done it until you can't do it anymore!

Congratulations! You have created a solid base of understanding and helped your students establish a firm sense of numbers. The process may not have been quick, and you may have hit a few glitches here and there, but you are now ready to give your students a new experience to let them create and explore a number using a number bracelet. A number bracelet is simply a number of pony beads on a chenille stem (aka a pipe cleaner). This inexpensive and effective tool, which we learned about from our friend and colleague Catherine Kuhns, helps students see the relationship between the parts and the whole in another concrete way; they can then look at the whole and easily manipulate the parts by sliding the beads. We recommended a number bracelet for each number you're studying. Let your students make them; it will deepen their understanding of the number.

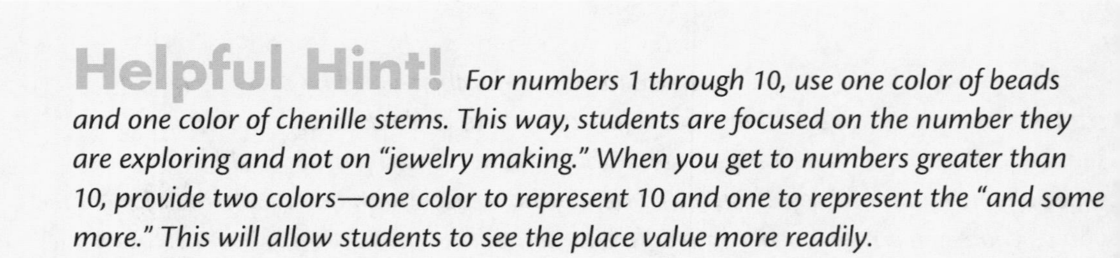

Helpful Hint! ***For numbers 1 through 10, use one color of beads and one color of chenille stems. This way, students are focused on the number they are exploring and not on "jewelry making." When you get to numbers greater than 10, provide two colors—one color to represent 10 and one to represent the "and some more." This will allow students to see the place value more readily.***

Once students create a number bracelet, have them look at it in two ways. Using our example of 5, students can first look at the number bracelet as 2 + 3 = 5. It can be useful to take them back to their "story of" experience to make that connection.

But you can also flip the bracelet over and see that 3 + 2 = 5. This leads to the understanding that 5 = 2 + 3 and 5 = 3 + 2. This models the Commutative Property of Addition and provides a powerful learning experience that will help prevent one of the most common misconceptions of students—the idea that the whole can't come at the beginning of an equation. Have you ever seen a student who knows that 2 + 3 = 5, but when presented with 5 = 2 + ______ will write 7? The idea that an equal sign means "you combine things" or "an answer is coming" is something that appears often. Working with number bracelets provides a chance to clear up that misconception right away. It won't happen overnight, but it will happen.

Students can use a journal page or two to draw their number bracelet representations to further develop and enhance their understanding of the number combinations discovered, such as 5 = 2 + 3 and 5 = 3 + 2. (See pages 153–157 for a reproducible Addition Journal.) This journal task makes a simple and smooth transition from the concrete to the pictorial representation of each relationship. This step also helps students connect what they already know with the **concept of number bonds** in a more abstract way than the work we've been doing thus far with manipulatives and journal pictures.

concept of number bonds (n):

understanding how numbers "bond" together by composing and decomposing them into their part-to-whole relationship

Students can now draw pictures and record math facts in a more formal way or in any way that makes sense for them at that moment. For example, you may have students first draw and then later record their bonds. Or you might want to have them draw their pictures and record bonds simultaneously. You can also challenge your higher-level learners by having them record the equations that support the number bracelet pictures.

A fun supporting children's literature book to use while you work with number bracelets is Equal Shmequal *by Virginia Kroll and illustrated by Philomena O'Neill.*

The inexpensive and effective tool of number bracelets helps students see the relationship between the parts and the whole in a concrete way. Students begin with counting out the beads, and then they show you what they know as you ask them what different combinations can make 5 and by flipping over the bracelet to reflect the Commutative Property. Students can also use their bracelets later as they work on abstract paperwork. All of these different opportunities lead students to continue developing their sense of numbers.

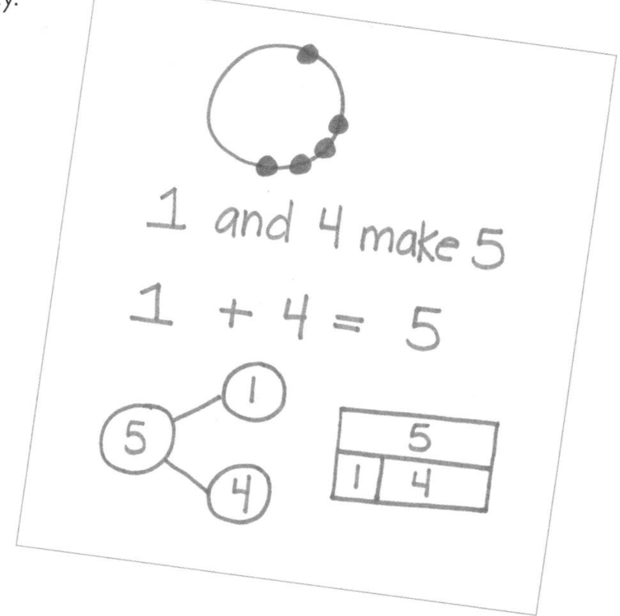

It's important to remember that throughout this entire process, you'll be talking about and teaching both addition AND subtraction. They aren't isolated operations; they are interconnected.

Anchor Charts

Anchor charts can be used here as a model for students' thinking. The purpose for making these charts is for students to see the number, the parts that can make up the number, AND the multiple representations that show the different combinations that make up the number.

You can help students deepen their understanding of these concepts by creating anchor charts that show the part-part-whole relationship and the related language. Create anchor charts on the spot; resist the urge to create a really pretty one and laminate it for use year after year. Let each chart be a representation of THIS class's learning and understanding. Students can also recreate the anchor charts in their math journal. This process helps hold them accountable for the learning of the concept. In other words, you don't have to create the entire chart all at once. Start with one idea or concept and add to it as your students are ready to take their understanding to the next level. As students develop understanding, you can attach or substitute the correct mathematical language.

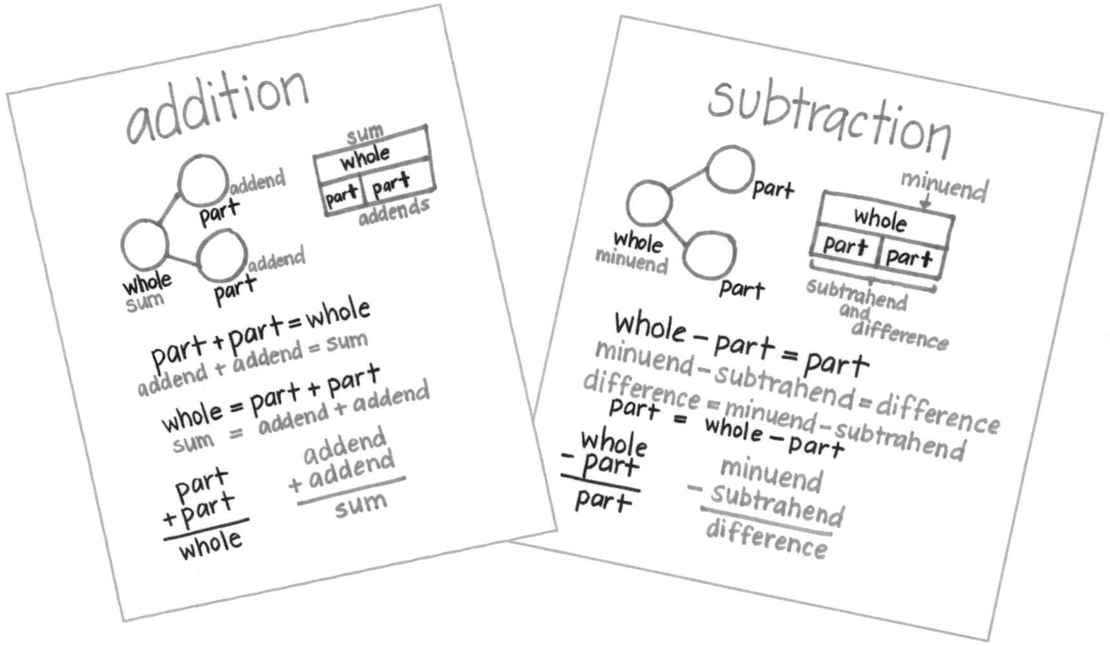

Helpful Hint! *If you can find a copy of it, one of our favorite pieces of children's literature that helps show how numbers can be composed and decomposed is* 12 Ways to Make 11 *by Eve Merriam and illustrated by Bernie Karlin.*

Here's an example of a large 8 featuring some of the "ways to make 8" as recorded by students. Teachers could create a large 8 on an anchor chart; students could create their own version in their journals; or this could be used as inspiration for a class book.

We have found that a fun and effective way to incorporate the entire class's anchor charts into one project is to create a class book titled, ***25 Ways to Make Numbers*** (changing the "25" to match the total number of students in your class). Assign each student a number specifically chosen for the child based on her or his abilities and needs. For example, you might have a struggling student create an anchor chart for the number 4, but assign the number 24 to a more capable student. Each student creates a page for the book that can be read and reread throughout the year. Often, these class books are the most popular published books in the room!

Divided Plates

Your main goal when trying to help your students become fluent in addition and subtraction is to help them obtain a deep understanding of part-part-whole. You can help make this understanding easier to achieve through the use of manipulatives. For example, we can visually conceptualize the part-part-whole relationship using a very simple manipulative such as a plate that is divided into three parts.

The beautiful thing about the divided-plate manipulative and strategy is that it can transcend basic addition and subtraction and can carry students through into fractions and decimals. Once students see this as a part-part-whole relationship and are able to make accurate generalizations to other concepts, their learning possibilities are endless.

concrete (adj):

using hands-on manipulatives to deliver math instruction conceptually (i.e., teddy bear counters, base-10 blocks, bean sticks, etc.)

pictorial (adj):

representing numbers, equations, or word problems with pictures or other visual representations (i.e., drawn pictures of items, model drawing, bar models, tape diagrams, strip diagrams, etc.)

abstract (adj):

the final stage in the math continuum where students demonstrate an understanding of the process by solving the problem with an algorithm

C-P-A

As with any sequence of delivery, we will begin with actual items and then transition to abstract numbers. Teachers can move through the **concrete**, **pictorial**, and **abstract** delivery from actual items (teddy bear counters or pennies), to items that represent real items (connecting cubes, tiles, base-10 blocks), and then eventually to bars or pictures that represent those items and numbers but may not have a one-to-one correspondence.

We can also help students by moving from proportionally sized items that are groupable (paper clips or connecting cubes) to proportional items that are pre-grouped (base-10 blocks). In time, we can move to non-proportional, not already-grouped items (straw bundles), and finally to non-proportional, already-grouped items (place value disks or money).

Throughout this progression, it is important to teach the students in front of you. We need to modify our instruction and choose our methods for the kids we have, not the students we want. Through careful observation, you will know what they need, and you must choose the right strategy for the right student at the right time. That includes providing the most appropriate manipulatives for the given purpose and activity.

Helpful Hint! *Concrete-Pictorial-Abstract—Look for the CPA line at the beginning of each game and activity. There will be a C for concrete, P for pictorial, or A for abstract. This will indicate which reasoning each activity or game develops.*

Progression Example

Based on the C-P-A sequence described in the previous paragraphs, the progression of manipulatives might look something like this:

Groupable models ***could also include items like straws, beansticks, Unifix cubes, etc.*** Students can take individual units and group them and/or bundle them to show groups of 10.	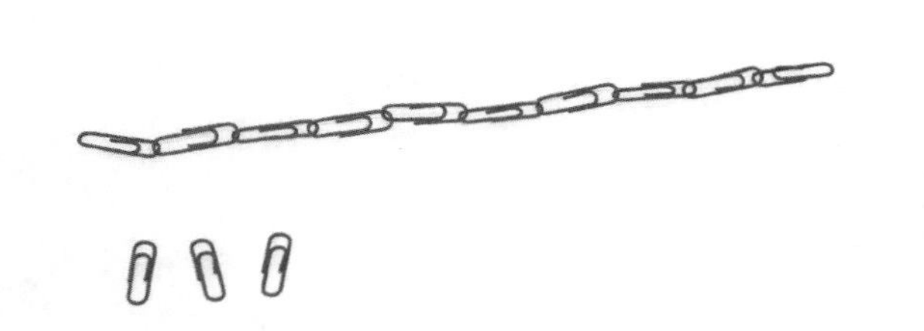
Pre-grouped models ***base-10 blocks, money, etc.*** Students can trade one stick of 10 for 10 individual units. It is important for students to recognize that 10 units can be traded for one larger unit equal to 10.	

Proportional models (K–1) ***Unifix cubes, cups and beans, etc.*** Students can take individual units and group them and/or bundle them to show groups of 10.	
Non-proportional models ***place value disks, cereal of different colors, etc.*** Students understand the value of 10 individual items is equal to one piece equivalent to 10. The size may be the same, but the value is different.	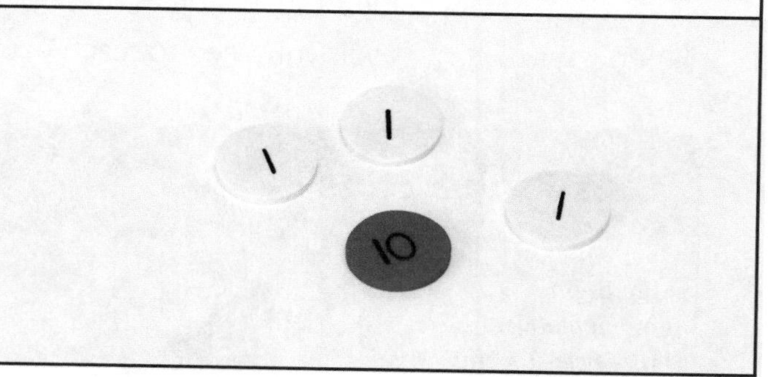

Helpful Hint! *Don't let the lack of the "right" manipulative stop you from doing the right instruction. You'll notice that some of the manipulatives listed are easily and readily available in your classroom and even from your local grocery store. The important concept to make clear to students is the idea that numbers can be composed and decomposed. We want varied opportunities for them to explore this concept.*

As you progress through the numbers, it is important to help students make connections to 10 so they continue to develop number sense on the way to fluency. For example, when working with the number 5, some questions to facilitate thinking might include the following:

- What does 5 look like in comparison to 10?
- How does 5 fill up a 10-frame?
- How does 5 look on a **rekenrek**?
- What might a train of **Cuisenaire rods** look like to create and make 5?
- Can you think of another way to show 5?

rekenreks (n):

arithmetic racks made up of rods and beads

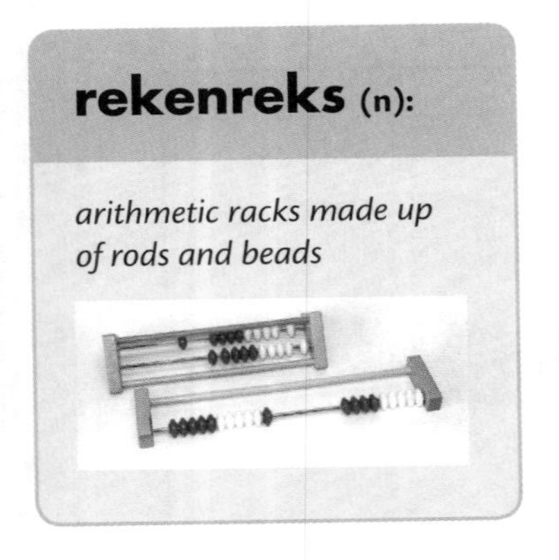

It's important to understand that, despite our suggested order, when teaching any given concept, there really isn't one right manipulative to use. In fact, research shows that short, varied practice is important for learning. If we only use one type of manipulative, we run the risk of students learning ***how*** to use the manipulative versus knowing the concept we were hoping to teach ***with*** the manipulative. This idea also reinforces that no matter where you teach, you have (or can find) the tools you need to teach your students.

Cuisenaire rods (n):

hands-on manipulatives that help students learn mathematical basics

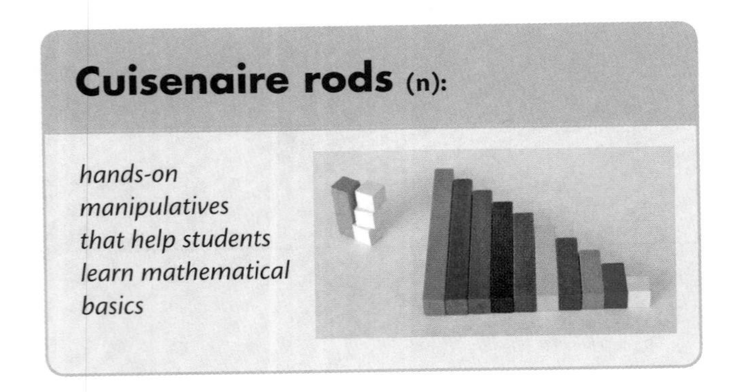

Often, teachers think, "If I just had (insert the latest and greatest manipulative here), then I could teach." But that's a fallacy; it's the instruction that matters, not the tool. You may ask: ***But what if I have no formal math manipulatives? What could I use to teach the concept? Could I use beans?*** Of course! ***Could I use egg cartons with two sections cut off so a dozen becomes 10?*** Of course! Once you get thinking, the possibilities are endless. Stay true to the purpose of your instruction, and you just can't go wrong.

Real-Life Application

As students see the relationship between numbers, their parts, and their relationship to 10, we can move on to context. Context and application, after all, are how we use math in our day-to-day lives. Most of the math we do daily is within a context. We're adding up the total cost of groceries we bought, or the total score of a ball game we're watching, or the number of cans needed to reach the goal in a canned food drive.

Now is the time to translate number stories into real-life scenarios. Ask your students to create a story using the number in a real-life situation. For example, a number story for 5 could be, "If Gertrude the pug eats two dog treats, and Gus the pug eats three dog treats, how many dog treats did the pugs eat?" Real-life application is a powerful way to deepen and solidify the understanding already established from past work. It's important to keep in mind that just as writing develops in English Language Arts, we must begin with oral practice through verbal rehearsals. After students are more competent, they can then move on to frames and sentence structures, finally being able to produce their own number story independently.

Helpful Hint! *As an ongoing classroom routine, provide a picture that students can color and use when writing their number story. This can also be a scaffold for a student who needs support finding the real-life connection. A fun homework assignment is to instruct students to find a picture that would work for the daily math story. Photocopy the picture (if appropriate and with permission, of course), and use it for inspiration with your entire class.*

Students can also be asked periodically to write a number story as part of a group. This activity provides the opportunity to collaborate while using the math practice of "constructing a viable argument and critiquing the reasoning of others" to get their point and their choices across to others.

Addition Strategy Book

Once students have a solid concept of a number, you can add to their schema, or background knowledge, and develop other ways to think about putting numbers together and taking numbers apart. We do this by teaching students very specific, very purposeful, and very powerful strategies to make sense of addition problems that will help them also understand the inverse—subtraction.

As you teach the strategies, consider pausing after each and having students add their new strategy to their very own, homemade addition strategy book.

Students love little books. Teachers love students to have a variety of strategies to draw from. Why not combine the two?

This foldable is an oldie, but goodie. It's a single-sheet book that requires no tape and no staples. Students must follow the directions carefully to get their books to turn out, so the book-making process is a great formative assessment for listening. As you teach strategies using manipulatives, help students make accurate generalizations. They can then add sound, dependable strategies to their book.

Note: While making these books, encourage students to make strong corner-to-corner matches and pinch and slide their nails or a ruler along the creases to ensure they are strong. It will make the final squishing step much easier.

Addition Strategy Book

Materials: *copy paper, scissors*

Directions:

1. Fold the paper in half to make a half-sized, skinny landscape (also known as a hotdog fold, but try to use the language of math or technology).

2. Fold the half-sized landscape in half again and half again to create an eighth-sized portrait.

3. Open the folded paper back up to the original piece of paper and lay it as a portrait.

4. Fold the paper in half to create a half-sized landscape.

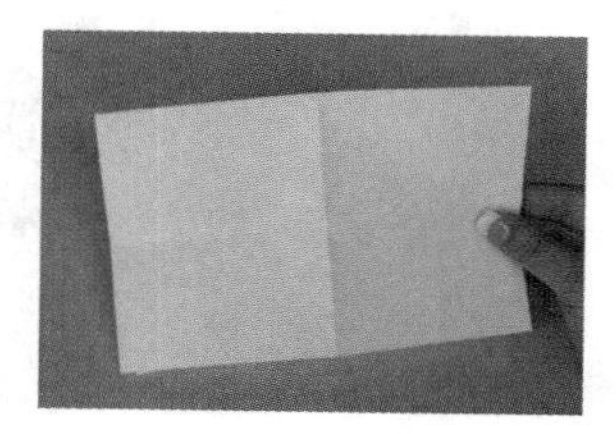

5. Place the fold toward you and cut from the midpoint of the fold to the intersection of the folds (half way into the folded paper).

6. Open up the paper and refold it to the half-sized skinny landscape.

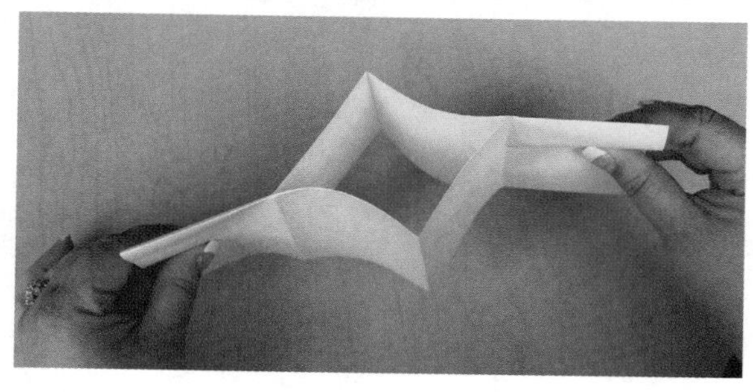

7. Hold both ends of the half-sized skinny landscape and push to create a rhombus-shaped opening. Keep pushing until there is no hole.

8. Now, "squish" the four folds together and crease the "spine" to create your eight-page book.

Helpful Hint! *When having students pinch and slide their fingers along folds, consider having them count by numbers while doing this. For example, "let's count by 2s from 16: 16, 18, 20 . . . " You can vary the count-bys as needed, and start from a variety of numbers.*

Here is an example of what a finished Addition Strategy Book could look like. Notice how we added playful images and bright colors. Allow students to do the same, and they will stay engaged and have fun all while deepening their understanding!

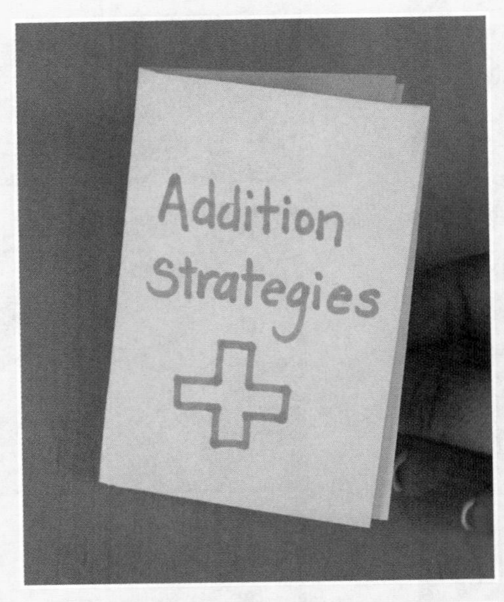

Have a few pre-made books ready for students who might struggle with the assembling process. Allow them their best effort, but rather than slowing down the entire class, hand them a pre-made book when you're ready to add strategies.

If you think you might use these books again for something else (for example, "Group It" from *Math Play*), have students estimate how many books they think they can make in about five to seven minutes, then let them go for it! At about the halfway mark let students revise their estimates. You'll end up with enough books to use for a long time. Gather the completed books into bundles of 10, compare estimates to actual, and put books away for another math activity or project at a later date.

Suggested Order of Strategies

The following chart is a suggested order for presenting concepts and ideas when teaching addition. We have found it to be the most effective because the concepts build on each other, but only you can determine which order is best. Typically textbooks allow for one or two days on each of these strategies. For most students, this pace is too fast; some strategies might take several weeks for them to completely comprehend. Time and understanding will be much more valuable to students' overall fluency success than pushing them through strategy after strategy as quickly as we can. Revisit all strategies frequently.

Identity Property of Zero. By beginning with 0 (for which students have an intuitive sense) and Zero Facts, you can move on to Turn Around Facts and the Commutative Property, building on students' experience with the "story of" and number bonds.

The next step would be Counting On. This strategy is important for the adding on of small addends. However, explain to students this method should not be used for counting on for large addends; it's not the most effective strategy as the addends get larger.

Next comes Doubles and Doubles + 1. Be sure to spend plenty of time on these two concepts. Both of these ideas are powerful connections that can be useful mental math strategies with both small and large numbers. They will also support their understanding with multiplication facts later.

Making a 10 should be somewhat familiar as students had exposure to this idea earlier, only now they can see it as a formal addition and subtraction strategy.

Fast 10s This is a great next step from making a 10. If students have become familiar with making a 10 as described in the strategy before, they can see the 10. They know what 10 is. They should be able to visualize this 10 as a stick of 10 with base ten units, a popsicle stick with 10 beans on it, or a 10-frame that is full. So an addition problem presented to them as 10 + 4, can easily be seen as 10 and some more. Automaticity for facts that have an already designated 10 (i.e. 10 + 7, 8 + 10) will quickly develop.

Part-Part-Whole is a piece that works alone and also with all other strategies. Students can always use this relationship to help them find the missing part (be it the addend that's missing, or the whole (sum), or later the whole (minuend) and parts (subtrahend and difference) in subtraction).

The last strategy explores the Associative Property. Ultimately, we want students to see that numbers can associate in any order to come up with the same sum.

Strategy	Description	Example
Zero Facts	Any number plus 0 equals the same number	16 + 0 = 16 0 + 16 = 16 16 = 0 + 16
Turn Around Facts (Commutative Property)	Flip the addends...the sum doesn't change	3 + 5 = 8 and 5 + 3 = 8
Counting On	Think about the larger addend, count on for +1, +2, and +3	5 + 2 = Think 5...6...7
Doubles	The same number added together	4 + 4 = 8 5 + 5 = 10
Doubles + 1	Add 1 to the doubles fact	4 + 5 = Think 4 + 4 = 8 8 +1 more = 9
Make a 10	Create a 10 and add on	8 + 4 = Think 8 + 2 = 10 10 + 2 = 12
Fast 10s	See the 10 and add on the "some more"	10 + 4 = Think 10 and 4 more makes 14.
Part-Part-Whole	Part + Part = Whole	8 2 | 6
Combine Numbers (Associative Property)	Find combinations that are easier to add	8 + 6 + 2 = Think 8 + 2 = 10 10 + 6 = 16

"But what might this look like in the classroom?" you may wonder.

What it ***doesn't*** look like is a timed test or handing out flashcards for students to memorize with no conceptual experience under their belt. To develop that conceptual experience, students need to make, move, and manipulate the numbers they'll be combining.

For the purpose of this book, we're going to assume students understand one-to-one correspondence and the relationship between item and number. If they don't, go back to the concrete and work, work, work!

However, if you've been doing the previously suggested activities, students should be ready to rock and roll with strategies! Let's dive in and take some time to explore each strategy from the chart in detail.

Use the following activities to develop the concept of adding and subtracting through a variety of strategies to go up to and beyond 10. Remember that subtraction is the inverse of addition, so, in most circumstances, you can use a similar activity with a focus on subtraction rather than the provided examples of addition.

The Identity Property of Zero

Let's start with Zero Facts, also known as the Identity Property of Zero. Students actually acquire this fact set quite quickly, and, interestingly enough, it will be one they'll be able to use for the rest of their math career.

You can make a big deal of having students start with five items.

- Have students add 0, and ask them what happens? Write that down.
- Then move on to eight items. Add 0. What happens?
- Have students investigate what happens when you add 0 to all of their numbers from their journal. Ask: ***Does the same thing always happen?***

Let students discover this unique property through exploration on their own. A helpful journal prompt at this time could be: ***Prove what we've discovered—that any number plus 0 equals the number. Show at least five examples.*** Add some engagement by including a really large number and seeing if students see that any number added to 0 results in the same number.

Another fun way to develop this property naturally is to play a favorite game entitled Rock, Paper, Scissors, Math. Not only will this sharpen their math fact skills in general, but it becomes the perfect opportunity for students to learn, through experience, the Identity Property of Zero.

This is the gist of the game, which is really just a version of Rock, Paper, Scissors, but with a mathematical twist:

- Two opponents face each other. Each taps his or her fist into the palm of their other hand three times, saying with each tap, "rock," then "paper," and then "scissors."
- Then, on the fourth beat, both say "Math!" (or "Sums!" if playing to only practice addition) and place a number of fingers on their palm.
- Players quickly find the sum in their heads and try to say the sum before their opponent. The first person to state the correct sum wins the round.

This game is fun and purposeful in and of itself, but sooner or later a student will figure out that he can throw a 0 (no fingers at all, or a closed fist on his palm) and then only have to look at his partner's throw to immediately know the sum. Note: The phrase, "That's cheating!" may come up, but this is where, as a teacher, you seize the moment and maximize the teaching opportunity. You can explain that other mathematicians noticed this, too, and it's something called the Identity Property of Zero. So now, they know from today and forever, that whenever a number is added to 0, they'll immediately know the answer. We want students to know it's not cheating to use patterns to develop efficiency.

Your enthusiasm for these zero facts will help make any practice they do, not perfect, but more likely to become permanent. When you feel the time is right, you should say, "We won't be using the zero facts when playing Rock, Paper, Scissors, Math since we ***know*** our zero facts so well, but we'll keep practicing our other facts!"

Commutative Property (Turn Around Facts)

Once students are comfortable with Zero Facts, you may move on to Turn Around Facts, known by mathematicians as the Commutative Property. Teaching these facts takes a while, so don't get frustrated. As previously mentioned, the number bracelets are a perfect way to model this property, and, after students' earlier experiences with the bracelets, pulling this tool back out to formally teach the strategy of Turn Around Facts and the Commutative Property is perfect timing and creates a great connection to their background knowledge. But there are other manipulatives you can use to help students understand this property: building the facts with two colors of connecting cubes, blocks, or Cuisenaire rods and turning them around also models the concept that the whole didn't change; the parts or addends didn't change, so, therefore, the answers or sums don't change.

The more you can do with this property, the better. All too often, when students just memorized facts, they would know that 5 + 4 = 9, but then when presented with 4 + 5 = ?, they'd be stumped. This is not unique to addition, so if we help them to truly recognize and understand the Commutative Property of Addition, they'll be able to generalize and apply this understanding at other times during their study of math in subsequent grade levels. The hope is they'll recognize that they can switch the order to be more efficient and expand the facts they know.

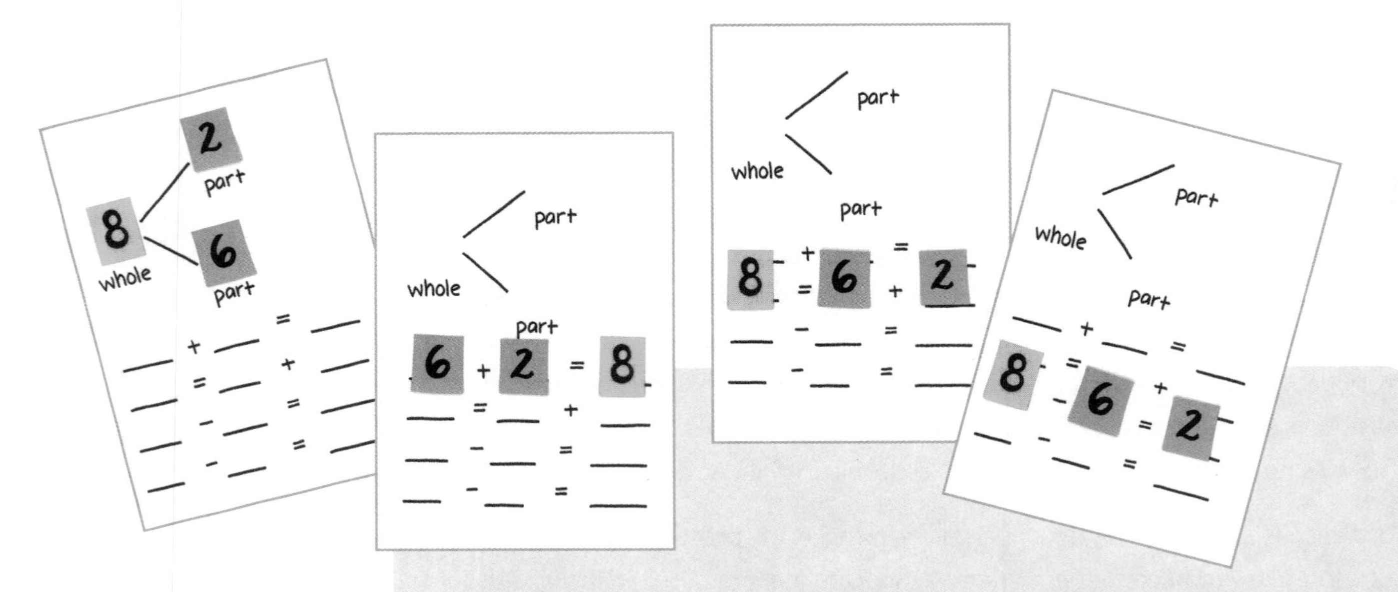

Another great teaching tool to help teach the Commutative Property is—believe it or not—your basic sticky note! (We learned this from our friend and colleague Char Forsten.) You can place numbered sticky notes into a number bond and then show students that in moving or flipping the sticky notes, the parts and whole don't change. You can then move the sticky notes into equations to show that the same numbers are present creating the same results.

So, for example, these sticky notes show that 2 + 6 = 8 and 8 = 6 + 2. But they also show that 8 - 6 = 2 and 8 - 2 = 6. This is the bonus of using this manipulative: Not only does it show students the Commutative Property of Addition, but it also demonstrates that if you know your addition facts, you know your fact family. It's a great reminder about the connection between addition and subtraction as well.

Counting On

Counting On is an important next strategy and—a word of warning—it can be one that becomes a crutch if not taught thoroughly and then talked about in depth. It's critical that your students know when Counting On is the best strategy to use, or when another strategy would better serve them for a specific purpose.

The key with this strategy is for students to recognize the greatest addend and then count on from it. Too often students count on from the first number that they see, and then end up counting more than they are adding.

You can use two dice to demonstrate to students the power of Counting On.

- First, have students roll the dice.
- Next, have them choose the larger addend rolled and say this number aloud.
- Then, they use the other rolled number, or addend, to count on aloud.

For example, if I rolled a 5 and a 3, I would take the 5 in my hand, say, "5" aloud, and then count on "6, 7, 8" for the remaining 3. The key is in recognizing the larger addend and knowing to start counting there. All too often students will mistakenly first count up to 5 and then on to 8. Fluency won't be the focus if students aren't counting UP; if students are just counting, they need more support, practice, and time.

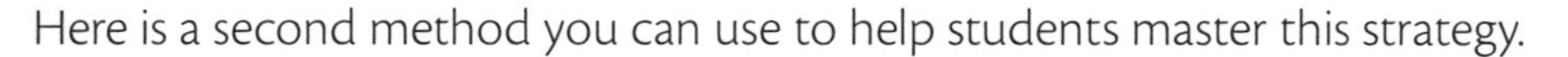

Here is a second method you can use to help students master this strategy.

- Begin by having students make a T chart. The left column is for the larger addend, and the right column is for the counting-on addend.
- Students roll two dice or turn over two playing cards.
- They record the addends in the appropriate columns, and practice counting on.

With practice, they will get into the habit of recognizing and using the larger addend and then counting on. Please remember, however, to emphasize that this is the best strategy to use when counting on by 1, 2, and 3. We use a different strategy (coming soon) to count on with numbers larger than 3.

Doubles and Doubles + 1

By the time students begin to work on Doubles and Doubles + 1, their repertoire of strategies is almost complete, and they should begin to feel very powerful as they can look at an addition fact and think, ***What strategy do I know to help me solve this?*** If they're not asking this on their own, you can model the practice for them to get them in the habit. You could "think aloud" and say, "When I see an addition fact, I think . . . hmmmm . . . do I know this from memory, and if not, what strategy do I know to help me solve this?" After students use this strategy enough times, they will develop automaticity. Remember what we said earlier: **Move slow now so we can move fast later.**

There are a lot of fun approaches you can take to teach the Doubles strategy. Many teachers teach visualization techniques to help students think of the facts. For example, 1 + 1 = 2, it's the eyeballs, and students can point one finger to each eye. A friend and colleague, Jane Felling, calls 1 + 1 the goal post fact. She's got actions for each of the Doubles, and her approach is extremely effective. These actions should not be taught as "tricks," but rather as visual or kinesthetic cues to help develop understanding. Be creative! A mixture of novelty, fun, and fundamentals will help students make these Doubles facts stick in their memory, and once they know them from memory, the facts become more and more fluent.

Here's a method you can use for students who learn best while using their hands: Have students build a stack of cubes, and then double it. This action can help them see what it means to double, and conversely, they can see what it means to halve something.

Helpful Hint! *A favorite children's literature piece to use during the teaching of doubling is* Two of Everything *by Lily Toy Hong. It's fun to have a pot in the classroom and model for students: "If I put two teddy bear counters in the pot and it doubles, what should come out? Four! If I put three sticky notes in the pot, what should come out? Six!" Students can create their own doubling book. To switch it up, students could also create a sequel titled,* Two of Everything Plus 1 *to illustrate the strategy of Doubles +1.*

Once students understand the concept of doubling, Doubles + 1 is a snap. Using just the verbal cue of, "Double it, plus 1!" can move students to including this strategy in their toolbox permanently. However, be sure to spend time on this concept. It will take a little bit longer for some students to master this strategy. But, it is a powerful mental math strategy, so we need to be sure we give all students a chance to understand and master it.

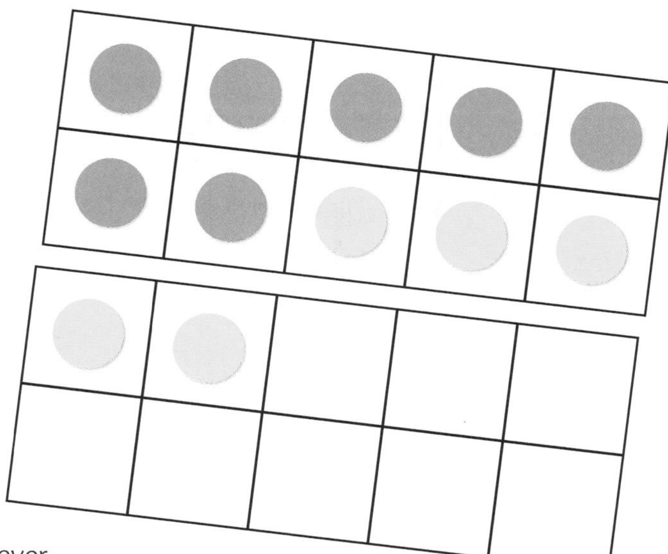

Make a 10

Make a 10 is a strategy that many of us have used forever, but we were never made aware of it in a formal, instructional way.

To teach students to Make a 10, consider taking students back to their number bracelets, their 10-frames, or Cuisenaire rods. Make the connection for students that in making a 10, we're simplifying the problem to something known (a 10) and then adding on, or, in other cases, we're thinking about the 10 and then subtracting down.

Here's an example using two number bracelets. Consider the problem 5 + 7.

- Set the 5 bracelet beside the 7 bracelet.
- Ask students to think about how they can make 10. They probably know 5 + 5 = 10, so they can use their 5 bracelet plus 5 beads from the 7 bracelet to make a 10, and then there are 2 beads remaining.
- Guide students to see that there's a 10 and 2 more for the answer of 12.

Some students may have also seen that 7 + 3 makes a 10. Using their 7 bracelet and three beads from their 5 bracelet, they have a 10 and 2 more, for the same answer of 12. The key with either approach is making 10 first and counting on from there.

Following this, the same modeling used to Make a 10 using number bracelets could and should take place with a double 10-frame or a 20-bead rekenrek.

Revisit Part-Part-Whole

Now, we're back to the part-part-whole strategy. Students should have a lot of experience with this by now, and this is a great chance to revisit where you've been and to help them transition into the early stages of a **tape diagram**. This is also known as a bar model or strip diagram, and it shows all the ways a part-part-whole

tape diagram (n):

a visual representation that shows the relationship between quantities using rectangles as units relationship might be represented. As you work, connect back to all the previous work, charts, journal entries, etc. that you've been so diligently working on. This cycling back can be considered on-going cumulative review and can make connections for students who haven't made them yet, as well as deepen the understanding for those who have already seen the relationships.

Associative Property

Finally, we explore the idea of three addends. Now is the time we demonstrate and prove to students that the order of addends in addition is flexible. That flexibility is defined as the Associative Property of Addition.

For the initial modeling of the Associative Property, bring three students to the front of the room. Move them around or group them in different combinations. With each change ask: "Who is here? Has anyone changed?" Students will readily see and agree: The only thing you've changed is the order of students, not the students themselves or how many of them are up there.

Now give these same students standing in front of the class number cards to hold. As a class, find their total sum. Now, move them around in a variety of groupings, just as you did before. With each change, find the sum. Point out that while the order of the addends changed, the sum stays the same.

Plan your numbers carefully so students can use all of their previously learned strategies to help them find combinations. For example, students could put a double together; they might add two numbers and then count on; or they might make a 10. Be sure to emphasize that they can do this because of the Associative Property of Addition.

At this point, it's also nice to use previous tools and manipulatives and ask: "Can a number be composed and decomposed with three parts?" Students should be able to answer with confidence, "Yes it can!" What a powerful discovery they can see using their number bracelets, their sectioned plates, and/or their Unifix cubes.

Purposeful Practice

Once students have developed their conceptual understanding of addition and subtraction, you can begin to work on their efficiency with this understanding. It's time to help them take this understanding to their permanent memory and increase their ability to readily recall the facts.

It takes over 25 exposures to develop a habit!

We're suggesting you do this through purposeful practice. This doesn't mean finding time for it on Friday as a filler activity but rather making a conscious choice to set aside time every day to help move facts into students' memory. If you'd previously been using timed tests, these activities would replace them. If you haven't previously fit in purposeful practice, find the time—it's the kind of stuff worth spending time on!

One of the foundational researchers, Zoltan Dienes, believed in short, varied experiences and practice. Malcolm Gladwell also proposes in his book ***Outliers*** that it takes 10,000 hours to become a master. That, together with the well-known idea that it takes over 25 exposures to develop a habit, leads us to believe that giving students lots and lots of opportunities to play with their addition and subtraction facts makes perfect sense!

As we move into purposeful practice with the facts, we would be remiss if we didn't say that this work is arduous. Not all students will have "Ah-ha!" moments at the same time. Not all students will see ideas in the same way. It has been said that the best intervention is to reteach properly. So when a student isn't getting it yet, go back to the concrete and the pictorial and give him a full dose of a proper reteach. This may take some creative planning on your part with configurations of your guided-math groups, the math stations you're using, support personnel, volunteers, etc. But, make no mistake, you can do it! Think outside of the box; pull from ***your*** toolbox and ours to work within your unique constraints to allow all students the opportunity for understanding.

With good instruction ALL students CAN see the connections, the relationships between numbers, concepts, and strategies, and make meaning of the facts we want them to have in their brains to use from memory. With good instruction and a little patience, all students can attain fact fluency.

Fluency Folders

A resource we've found to be very successful for both addition/subtraction and multiplication/division is to have students create a personal fluency folder that allows them to set personal goals, practice their understanding at a rate appropriate to their grade level and learning style, and have their progress assessed individually and then celebrated as they progress closer and closer to their goal. Finally, students get the chance to play games to practice and to celebrate at a speed that works for them. This purposeful game-playing allows students to develop the efficiency component of fluency and to commit those facts to memory.

Materials: ***two sheets of 8 ½ x 11-inch paper, tape, glue, colored markers***

Directions:

1. Fold one piece of paper in half horizontally to create a long skinny landscape, also known as a hot dog fold. Fold that paper in half to create a fourth-sized landscape. Set it aside.

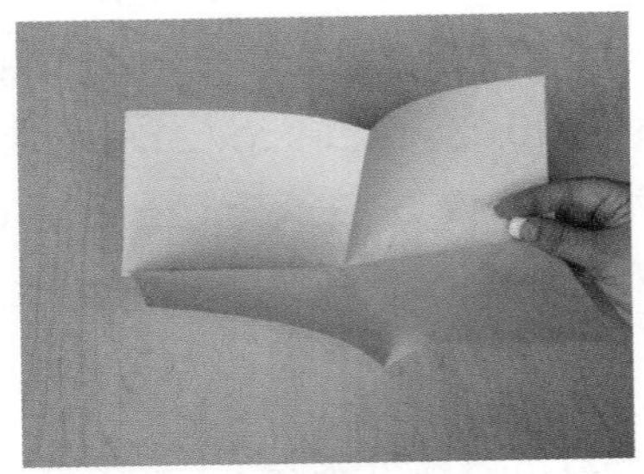

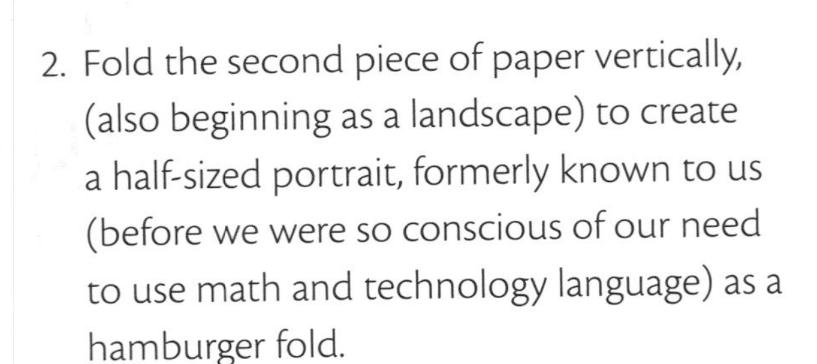

2. Fold the second piece of paper vertically, (also beginning as a landscape) to create a half-sized portrait, formerly known to us (before we were so conscious of our need to use math and technology language) as a hamburger fold.

3. Slide the half-sized portrait into the fourth-sized landscape to create a four-pocket folder—or—slide your "hamburger" into the "hotdog bun." It's easiest if you set your long, skinny landscape fold down and open, and then slide your half-sized portrait into that opening. This will create the folder.

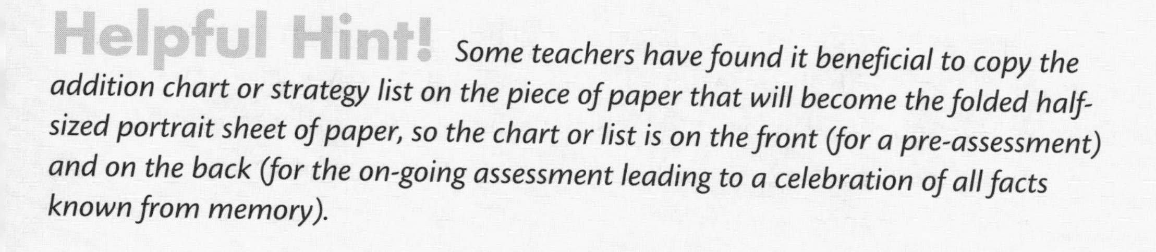

Helpful Hint! *Some teachers have found it beneficial to copy the addition chart or strategy list on the piece of paper that will become the folded half-sized portrait sheet of paper, so the chart or list is on the front (for a pre-assessment) and on the back (for the on-going assessment leading to a celebration of all facts known from memory).*

4. Tape each side of the pockets to prevent items from falling out the sides. One small piece of tape on each side is plenty.

5. Glue a small addition chart (Option 1) or list of addition strategies we've discussed earlier in this section (Option 2) on the front of the folder. Label that pocket Goals.

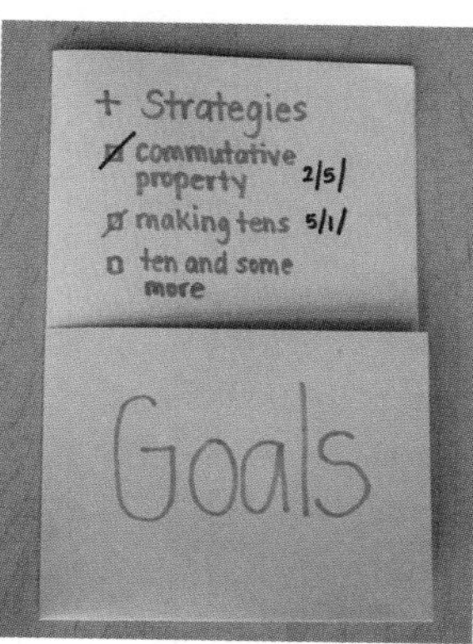

6. Open the folder. Label the left-hand side pocket of the inner folder Practice.

7. Label the right-side pocket of the inner folder Assess.

8. Close the folder. Label the back pocket Celebrate.

Using the Folders

Once students have finished their folders, you'll help them determine which facts they'll begin with. If you're using this as first instruction, you can move your students through the strategies and facts. If it is being used as an intervention, you may want to individualize even more for students which facts or strategies they're focusing on. Either approach has proved to be successful. Remember that each student will be working at his or her own pace.

Practice Cards

The front side of the practice card should be the traditional fact. The back side of the card can be a pictorial representation, or two, that supports the understanding of the fact. For example, if working on Making 10s, students might see it as a number bond and/or as a picture of two 10-frames. By thinking back on the strategies, figuring out the answer after some work, and having repeated exposure, they'll start to hold the facts in their memory!

To help students master the facts, have them create cards for one set of facts to practice until they are fluent. Remember how sight words are taught to students when they're beginning readers? This is a similar approach. Students should work on small, digestible chunks. They can play a "say-see-check" game in which the first student to get the problem correct keeps the cards (like the game Face Off on page 62). A variety of practice activities will ensure your students stay engaged and have fun.

Flash Facts Cards

For students who already have the conceptual understanding or are already showing proficiency with their math facts, flash facts cards, with addition on one side and the answers and subtraction practice on the other, are an effective and engaging option for practice.

Students can practice their facts until they believe they are fluent (fluency = understanding + accuracy + efficiency). They can use the flash facts cards by themselves, or with a partner because they are self-checking. The beauty of these cards is that they have a lot of facts on a single card.

Helpful Hint!

Flash Facts: On the addition side of the card, it's part + part = whole. On the subtraction side, it's whole (along the sides of the cards) subtract the part (the -5 as seen in the center of our example card), to find the difference (the other part on the back side of the tab).

Assessment Time

When students believe they're ready to be assessed, they move their practice cards or their flash fact cards over to the Assess part of their folder. By conducting a one-on-one oral assessment with the student, you have the opportunity to ask the child questions, such as:

- How did you know that answer?
- Did you use a certain strategy to solve that problem?
- Which strategy did you use?
- How did you know to use that strategy?

Having this conversation during the assessment will give you a lot more information about where the child is with her automaticity than an old-fashioned timed test. If the child is stuck, this is the perfect opportunity for you to jump in with reminders of strategies that can nudge her in the right direction. Again, our job as teachers is to educate our students and help them make progress toward their goals. If all we're doing is assessing without offering constructive feedback, how is the child expected to make the most growth possible?

Celebrate

If the student is fluent in a particular set of facts, those cards are moved to the Celebrate part of the folder. They then color in these newly memorized facts on their chart, or check off a proficient strategy (found on the front of their folder). Some teachers choose to use a different color for each set of facts learned and include a key to show the date at which those facts were obtained. For example, if Brett demonstrated fluency with his doubles, he would color in all of his double facts on his chart or check off Doubles on his strategy list in blue. A blue line would be placed beside the chart or list with the date 2/5 to indicate that on February 5, he showed you that he knew his doubles facts.

Helpful Hint! *Create a classroom space, such as a basket, for students to place their folder when they are ready to be assessed. Then, you can take the folders and the students who are ready and quickly check to see how they are progressing. This allows you to address students' needs on an individual basis. Keep in mind that some students may never let you know that they're ready to assess, so you may want to have a system for calling on students on a regular basis.*

Have Some Extra Time? Practice!

Give students a game to add to their Practice folder pocket so they always have something to work with. The half-sheet games at the back of this book are the perfect size. Working on their folders can be a warm-up once a week, a before-recess activity (you know, that weirdly empty five minutes that sometimes appear right before recess), or at a fluency workstation as part of your math rotations.

Consider keeping the folders at a fluency station in your classroom or have students keep their folders on their desk for easy access. If students are ever "just waiting" for whatever reason, have them develop the habit of using that time to work on their goals. You will soon see that the opportunities for practice are endless!

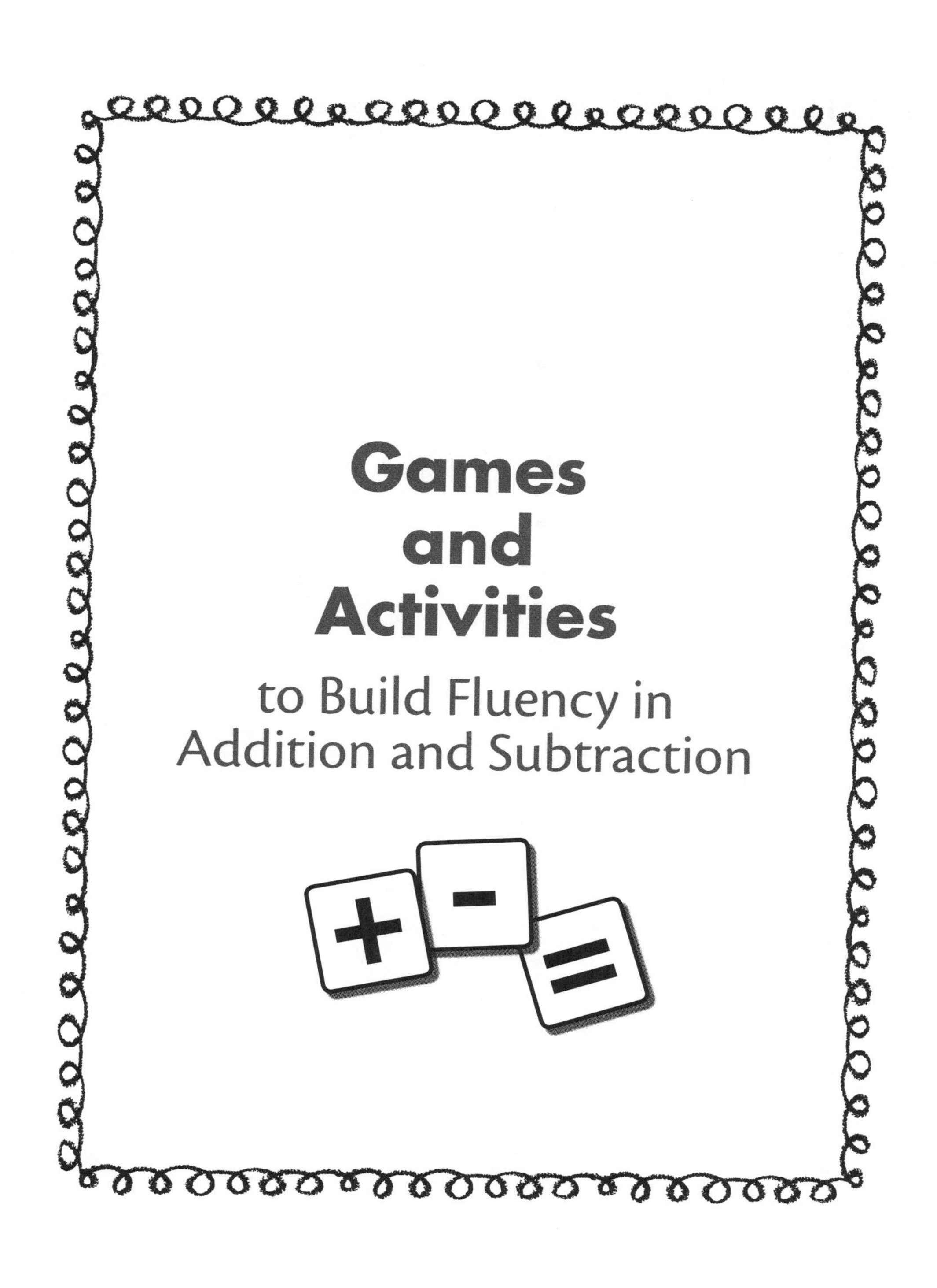

Games and Activities

to Build Fluency in Addition and Subtraction

Timely 10s

Objective: *Use the "Make a 10" strategy to add math facts; record number sentences*

Goal: *Make a 10*

Group Size: *Individual*

Materials: *double 10-frame board (on page 159), two-color counters or two different colors of another manipulative, Timely 10s recording sheet (on page 152), two 10-sided dice*

This activity provides practice in making 10s with each roll of the dice. Additionally, students will practice using 10-frames and recording the corresponding equations. A reduced facsimile for including in the Practice side of the fluency folders is available on page 138.

Note: If you do not have 10-sided dice, you could use number cards or use three regular 6-sided dice. Students will then roll three addends and use these addends to make 10 and record equations.

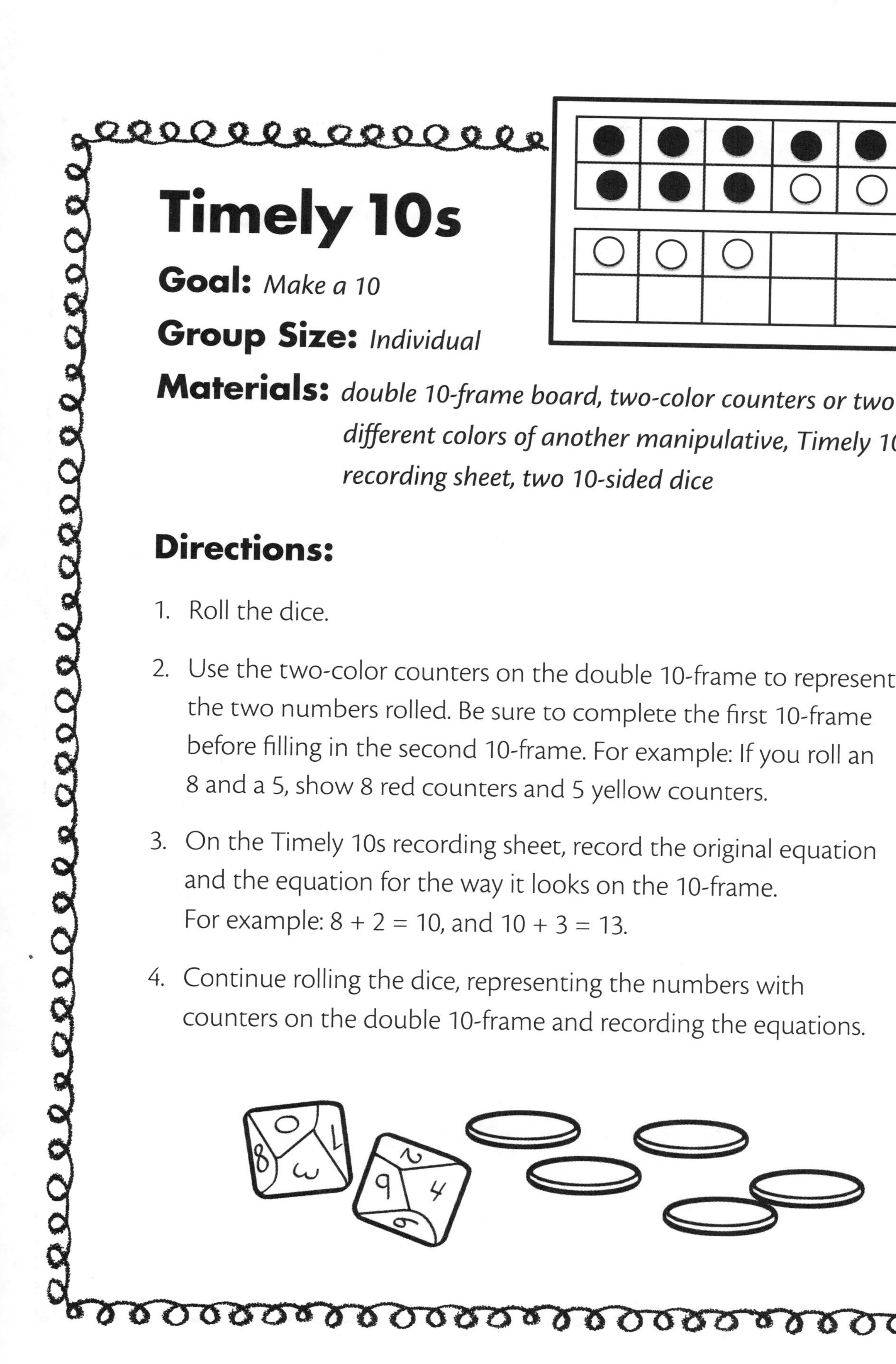

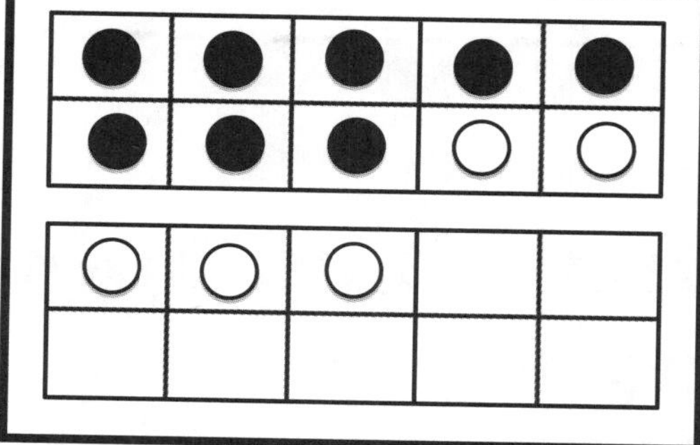

Timely 10s

Goal: *Make a 10*

Group Size: *Individual*

Materials: *double 10-frame board, two-color counters or two different colors of another manipulative, Timely 10s recording sheet, two 10-sided dice*

Directions:

1. Roll the dice.
2. Use the two-color counters on the double 10-frame to represent the two numbers rolled. Be sure to complete the first 10-frame before filling in the second 10-frame. For example: If you roll an 8 and a 5, show 8 red counters and 5 yellow counters.
3. On the Timely 10s recording sheet, record the original equation and the equation for the way it looks on the 10-frame. For example: $8 + 2 = 10$, and $10 + 3 = 13$.
4. Continue rolling the dice, representing the numbers with counters on the double 10-frame and recording the equations.

CPA: (A)

Sum-thing Special

Objective: *Practice adding two numbers together*

Goal: *Be the player with the highest total sum of cards at the end of the game*

Group Size: *Partners*

Materials: *two decks of cards with all face cards removed (Ace = 1)*

Here's a game that provides a fun way to practice adding two or more numbers, all while strengthening students' ability to perform mental math quickly. A reduced facsimile for including in the Practice side of the fluency folders is available on page 138.

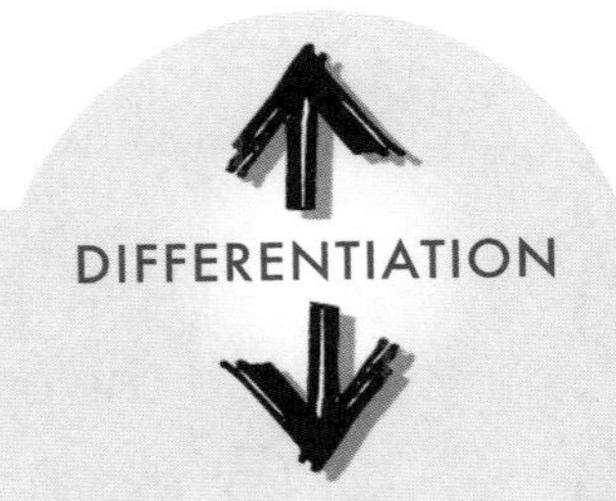

Switch It Up!

Here are some modifications you may wish to try:

- *Use number cards 1, 2, and 3 only to work on smaller sums.*
- *Have students put counters on the cards to use to find the sums. The player who has the highest sum collects the counters that are on the card on the right side. At the end, players will count their counters to see who has the most.*
- *For a challenge, have players lay out three cards and find the sum of these three addends. The right card still goes into their special pile, and the two other addend cards go to the bottom of the draw deck.*

Sum-thing Special

Goal: *Be the player with the highest total sum of cards at the end of the game*

Group Size: *Partners*

Materials: *two decks of cards with all face cards removed (Ace = 1)*

Directions:

1. Both players turn over two cards each at the same time. The cards should be placed side by side in front of the player—one card to the left side, and one card to the right side. Once the cards are placed, the order cannot be switched around. Each player adds her own cards together and says the sum.
2. The player who has the higher sum takes both cards that are in the right-side position (each player's right-side pile) and puts them off to the side into a special pile. Each player needs to keep her own special pile because it will be used later.
3. Players then put the card left on the table (the card that was on the left side) at the bottom of their draw pile.
4. Play continues until players are out of cards in their draw pile.
5. Now players collect all the cards from their special pile and add them together. The player with the greater sum wins.

CPA: (A)

Bowling for 10

Objective: *Practice making combinations of 10 (or any desired target number)*

Goal: *Be the player with the most points at the end of 10 rounds*

Group Size: *Partners*

Materials: *10 small paper cups, a marker, a tennis ball, recording sheet (located on page 149)*

This game allows students to get up, move around, and have some fun—all while strengthening their adding and tallying skills. A reduced facsimile for including in the Practice side of the fluency folders is available on page 139.

- It might be helpful and fun to invite students who have bowled before to explain to the class how to play.
- Take a moment to demonstrate how to roll (and not throw!) the ball for students before the games begin.

Switch It Up!

Here are some modifications you may wish to try:

- *Change the target number to any number students are working on; just change the numbers on the inside of the cups. For example, if you are working on combinations to 5, prepare or have students prepare the cups with two sets of 1–5.*
- *Allow students to use three addends to make the combination.*
- *For younger students, modify the game to focus on number recognition. On the outside of the cup draw a dot pattern and record the corresponding numeral on the inside of the cup (or dot pattern inside and numeral outside). Once the student rolls, he has to identify the number shown on the dot pattern for all of the cups that fall down.*

Bowling for 10

Goal: *Be the player with the most points at the end of 10 rounds*

Group Size: *Partners*

Materials: *10 small paper cups, a marker, a tennis ball, recording sheet*

Directions:

1. Before playing the game, prepare the cups by writing the numbers 1–10 on the outside of the cups. Place the cups in a bowling alley formation.
2. Player 1 rolls the tennis ball at the 10 cups. Player 1 uses the cups that fall down to make combinations to 10. On her recording sheet, Player 1 records one tally mark for every combination made.

   If all 10 cups are knocked over on the first try, Player 1 gets a bonus of five tally marks (similar to a strike in bowling), and then it's Player 2's turn. But if there are still cups standing, Player 1 moves to Step 3.
3. Player 1 rolls the ball again, knocks over more cups, and tries to make more combinations of 10. Newly knocked over cups can be combined with cups that have already been knocked over. Player 1 records one tally mark for each combination she makes.

   If all 10 cups are knocked over after this second roll, the player gets a bonus of two tally marks (similar to a spare in bowling).
4. When Player 1's turn is over, the cups are placed back in starting position, and Player 2 takes a turn following the directions in Steps 2 and 3.
5. Players take turns through 10 rounds.

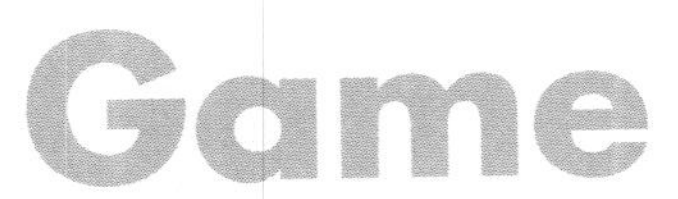

CPA: (A)

Deal a Double

Objective: *Strengthen and master doubles of 1 through 10*

Goal: *Be the player who has collected the most cards at the end of the game*

Group Size: *Small groups*

Materials: *a deck of cards with all face cards removed (Ace = 1)*

In this fast-paced game, students race to see who can mentally calculate and say the card's double. The Deal a Double version is for students who are still mastering their doubles facts; The Deal a Double +1 version as explained in Switch It Up! is for those who are ready for a bit more of a challenge. A reduced facsimile for including in the Practice side of the fluency folders is available on page 139.

Switch It Up!

Here are some modifications you may wish to try:

You can tailor this activity to help struggling students or challenge those who are ready to take doubling to the next level.

- *Create target decks for students to work on specific doubles such as 1–5.*
- *For students who have mastered doubling numbers 1 through 10, a modified version of this game called "Deal a Double +1" may be played. The dealer may say "Double!" or "Double +1!" when turning over a card. The first person to answer correctly gets the card.*
- *For those who need even more of a challenge, double the double (i.e., if the card was a 7, the double would be 14, and the double's double would be 28).*

Deal a Double

Goal: *Be the player who has collected the most cards at the end of the game*

Group Size: *Small groups*

Materials: *a deck of cards with all face cards removed* (Ace = 1)

Directions:

1. Sit in a way that allows each player to clearly see each card as it is being turned over.
2. One player turns over a card, and the watching students mentally double that card.
3. The first player to say the card's correct double gets to keep the card.
4. The deck is passed to the next player, and Steps 2 and 3 are repeated.
5. Play continues until all of the cards are gone.

NOTE: If there is any dispute about an answer, the dealer decides who is correct.

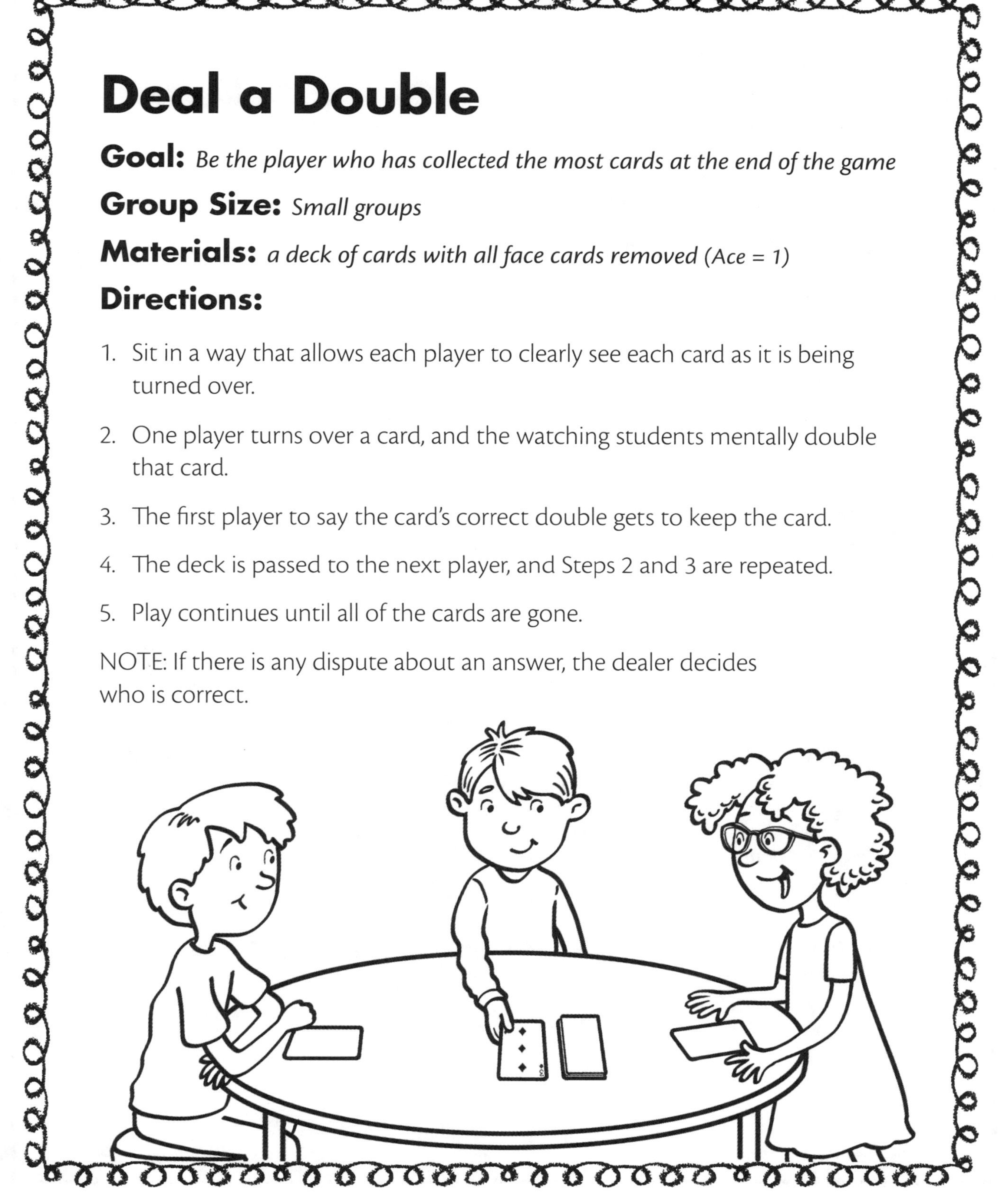

CPA: (A)

Exact-O-Mo

Objective: *Students will practice adding up and subtracting down mentally using worked-on strategies.*

Goal: *Be the player with the most points at the end of the game*

Group Size: *Partners*

Materials: *a deck of cards with all face cards removed (Ace = 1)*

This game was originally developed as a way to make use of mismatched, incomplete, or overly complete decks of cards. It still works great for that, by the way! Originally, the target number was always 25. However, a colleague pointed out that you could change the target number based on the students' abilities in front of you, and with that suggestion, the game morphed to Exact-O-Mo. Using whatever cards are available, students work to mentally add up or down to reach the exact number determined as the target number. It provides for oodles of opportunities for mental math practice and is best played with two like-skilled partners. A reduced facsimile for including in the Practice side of the fluency folders is available on page 140.

DIFFERENTIATION

Switch It Up!

Here are some modifications you may wish to try:

You can tailor this activity to help struggling students or challenge those who are ready to take doubling to the next level.

- *Lower or raise the target number to match student ability.*
- *If students struggle with mental addition, the decks could also be modified to include smaller numbers that are more easily added mentally.*

Exact-O-Mo

Goal: *Be the player with the most points at the end of the game*

Group Size: *Partners*

Materials: *a deck of cards with all face cards removed (Ace = 1)*

Directions:

1. Each player grabs a stack of cards. This does not need to be a complete deck, and it may exceed 52 cards.
2. Players agree on a target number between 20 and 50.
3. One player turns over a card in the center of the playing space. Player 1 then turns over another card, and then uses the two cards to say an addition equation. For example, if the first card was a 5, and the second card was a 7, Player 1 would say, "5 + 7 = 12." Player 2 determines if Player 1 is correct.
4. If the target number has not been reached, Player 2 turns over a card and adds it to Player 1's total. For example, if Player 2 turned over a 3, she would say, "12 + 3 = 15."
5. Players continue taking turns until the target number is reached. If the sum goes higher than the target number, the next player must subtract the flipped card. Once the total dips lower than the target number, players once again add flipped cards. This process continues until a player "hits" the target number exactly. The player who flips over the card that "hits" the target number gets a point.

Once the target number is reached, play starts at 0, and players take turns adding and subtracting to reach the target number again, playing for as long as time allows.

CPA: (A)

Doubles, Doubles + 1, Other Adding Fun

Objective: *Students work and strengthen their doubles and/or doubles + 1 skills*

Goal: *Correctly guess which strategy category will win*

Group Size: *Small group*

Materials: *a deck of cards with all face cards removed (Ace = 1), OR two 6-sided dice (easier version) or two 10-sided dice (more challenging), three-column chart (see page 147)*

Often students don't realize the power of strategies. They focus too much on memorization and lose sight of the fact that strategies can help them solve a problem when facts have been forgotten. This activity helps students recognize (and practice) the strategies of Doubles and Doubles + 1 for addition. These two powerful strategies can help them solve many problems and provide for some fun game-playing, too. A reduced facsimile for including in the Practice side of the fluency folders is available on page 140.

DIFFERENTIATION

Switch It Up!

Here are some modifications you may wish to try:

- *For students who still need pictorial support, consider using dominoes to support student understanding.*
- *For a challenge, have students use the data from the rolls or turned cards and graph the strategies using a grade-appropriate graph (e.g., a bar graph).*
- *Add more columns for additional strategies, such as Make a 10. NOTE: Make a 10 will only work if playing with all number cards, Ace (1) through 10 or two 10-sided dice.*

Doubles	Doubles +1	Other

Doubles, Doubles + 1, Other Adding Fun

Goal: *Correctly guess which strategy category will win*

Group Size: *Small group*

Materials: *a deck of cards with all face cards removed (Ace = 1), OR two 6-sided dice (easier version) or two 10-sided dice (more challenging), three-column chart*

Directions:

1. Each player takes a copy of the three-column chart labeled Doubles, Doubles + 1, and Other Adding Fun.
2. Each player makes a prediction about which column will "win"—meaning which strategy will be used the most. Will it be the Doubles strategy, the Doubles + 1, or the Other?
3. Player 1 rolls the dice or turns over two cards, and then determines which addition strategy will best serve them. For example, if the two numbers are 4 and 4, the best strategy would be Doubles, and Player 1 would write "4 + 4 = 8" in the Doubles column on his or her chart. If a 4 and 5 are rolled/turned over, the best strategy would be Doubles + 1 because "4 + 4 = 8 and one more is 9." If neither Doubles nor Doubles + 1 can be used to add the two numbers, then Player 1 would record the number sentence in the column Other Adding Fun.
4. Play continues until each player has taken a predetermined number of turns.
5. Players then total their columns and see if their prediction matched their outcome.

Game

CPA: (A)

Power Tower

Objective: *Practice addition facts*

Goal: *Collect as many cups as you can to build a tower*

Group Size: *Individual*

Materials: *small cups labeled with math facts on the outside, answers on the inside, a container to hold the cups*

Note: It is easiest to write the math fact on the bottom or outside of the paper cups, and then record the answer inside the cup. Consider using different colored containers to allow for differentiation. For example, the red containers only contain cups with sums to 5; the blue containers have sums to 10; the green containers have sums to 20. A reduced facsimile for including in the Practice side of the fluency folders is available on page 141.

Switch It Up!

Here are some modifications you may wish to try:

- *For students who aren't ready for math facts, prepare the cups with subitizing images.*
- *To keep struggling players engaged and motivated, mark several cups "two free cups." When the student comes to one of these cups, he gets to take that cup and the next one "for free" regardless of whether he knows the answer. Students will begin to accumulate cups and stay engaged.*
- *To challenge students who are ready for more, modify the game to include multiplication facts.*
- *Have students use different colored markers or cups, and allow pairs to work together to double the number of cups available.*

Power Tower

Goal: *Collect as many cups as you can to build a tower*

Group Size: *Individual*

Materials: *small cups labeled with math facts on the outside, answers on the inside, a container to hold the cups*

Directions:

1. Choose a container of cups and take it to your seat. Take the stack of cups out of the container.
2. Take the first cup from the top of the stack. Solve the math problem you see on the cup. Check inside the cup to see if you have the correct answer.
3. If you answered correctly, you get to keep the cup! If you did not answer correctly, return the cup to the bottom of the stack.
4. As you collect cups, build the highest or most interesting tower you can by stacking the cups you earned.

Your goal is to use all of the cups to build your tower!

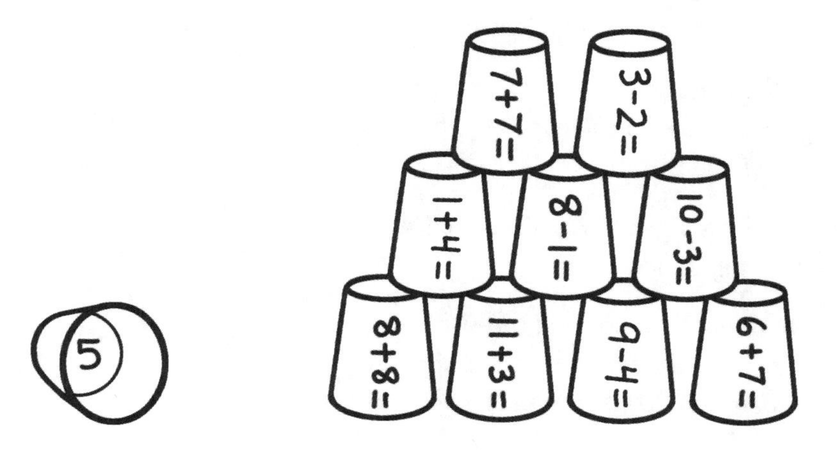

Rock, Paper, Scissors, Sums!

Objective: *Practice adding two numbers together*

Goal: *Be the player to win two out of three rounds*

Group Size: *Whole group, partners*

Materials: *None!*

Rock, Paper, Scissors, Sums! is a fast-paced, kinesthetic game that provides math fact fluency practice and the opportunity for students to get up and move. Before play begins, be sure to review how the traditional Rock, Paper, Scissors is played. Explain that this game is the same thing, but at the end, instead of making a rock, paper, or scissors, students will be making a number with their fingers on their other hand. These numbers will be added (or subtracted, or multiplied—depending on the version you choose for your students that day). A reduced facsimile for including in the Practice side of the fluency folders is available on page 141.

Note: Eventually, students will notice that if they throw a 0 (no fingers at all), they can find the sum faster (or product, if playing for multiplication). This isn't cheating—in addition, this is the Identity Property of Zero.

Here are some modifications you may wish to try:

- *Have players subtract the numbers that are thrown. The first player to call out the difference wins the round.*
- *Have players double their "throws" before they find the sum or difference.*
- *Tell players to use both hands and throw numbers flat on a table rather than on the other palm. This makes the addends up to 10 instead of 5.*
- *Instruct players to name the numbers and compare their values instead of adding or subtracting. As the teacher, roll a die that has "more" written on three sides and "less" written on three sides. Whichever shows on the die dictates who would win the round.*
- *For struggling students, simply have them say the number their partner threw; there would be no winner with this version, but there's a lot of practice!*
- *Play Rock, Paper, Scissors, Product! to practice multiplication facts (one hand for facts up to 5 x 5, two hands on the table for facts up to 10 x 10.*

Rock, Paper, Scissors, Sums!

Goal: *Be the player to win two out of three rounds*

Group Size: *Whole group, partners*

Materials: *None—just your hands!*

Directions:

1. Players can find the nearest partner or they can stand in two circles—one inner circle, and one outer circle. Players should stand facing each other and "partner up."
2. To play, the two partners say together, "Rock, paper, scissors, sums!" while tapping their fists into their palms—one tap each for "rock," "paper," and "scissors."
3. When players say "sums," each "throws" a number of fingers.
4. As quickly as they can, both players find the sum of the two numbers shown on their hands. The first player to say the correct sum wins that round.
5. Play continues with the same partner until a player wins two out of three rounds.
6. After three rounds, players in the outer circle rotate over one partner and play again.

Face Off

Objective: *Practice adding two numbers together*

Goal: *Be the player with the most cards at the end of the game*

Group Size: *Partners*

Materials: *a deck of cards with all face cards removed (Ace = 1)*

Face Off is a fast-paced game that will have your students practicing their math facts while having fun with their partner. This game is ideal for addition, subtraction, and multiplication. You may notice that this game closely resembles the classic card game "War." We've switched it up a bit, made it less about battling and more about adding! A reduced facsimile for including in the Practice side of the fluency folders is available on page 142.

Switch It Up!

Here are some modifications you may wish to try:

- *To shake things up, try modifying the directions like this: If the sum is more than 10, Player 1 gets the cards. If the sum is less than 10, Player 2 gets the cards. If the sum is exactly 10, each player turns over another card and adds the two new cards together. If the sum is more than 10, Player 1 gets all four cards. If the sum is less than 10, Player 2 gets all four cards.*
- *Have students subtract or multiply the two numbers that are showing on the cards.*
- *For students who are ready for a challenge, include the face cards and jokers as follows: Jokers = 0, Jacks = 11, Queens = 12, and Kings = 13.*

Face Off

Goal: *Be the player with the most cards at the end of the game*

Group Size: *Partners*

Materials: *a deck of cards with all face cards removed (Ace = 1)*

Directions:

1. Divide the cards evenly between both players.
2. Both players turn over their top card at the same time.
3. Each player mentally adds the two numbers and shouts out the sum as quickly as possible.
4. The first player to say the correct sum gets to keep both cards.
5. If it is a tie, both players turn over three more cards and try again. The first person to find the correct sum of the last cards turned over gets to keep all of the turned-over cards.
6. Play continues until one player is out of cards.

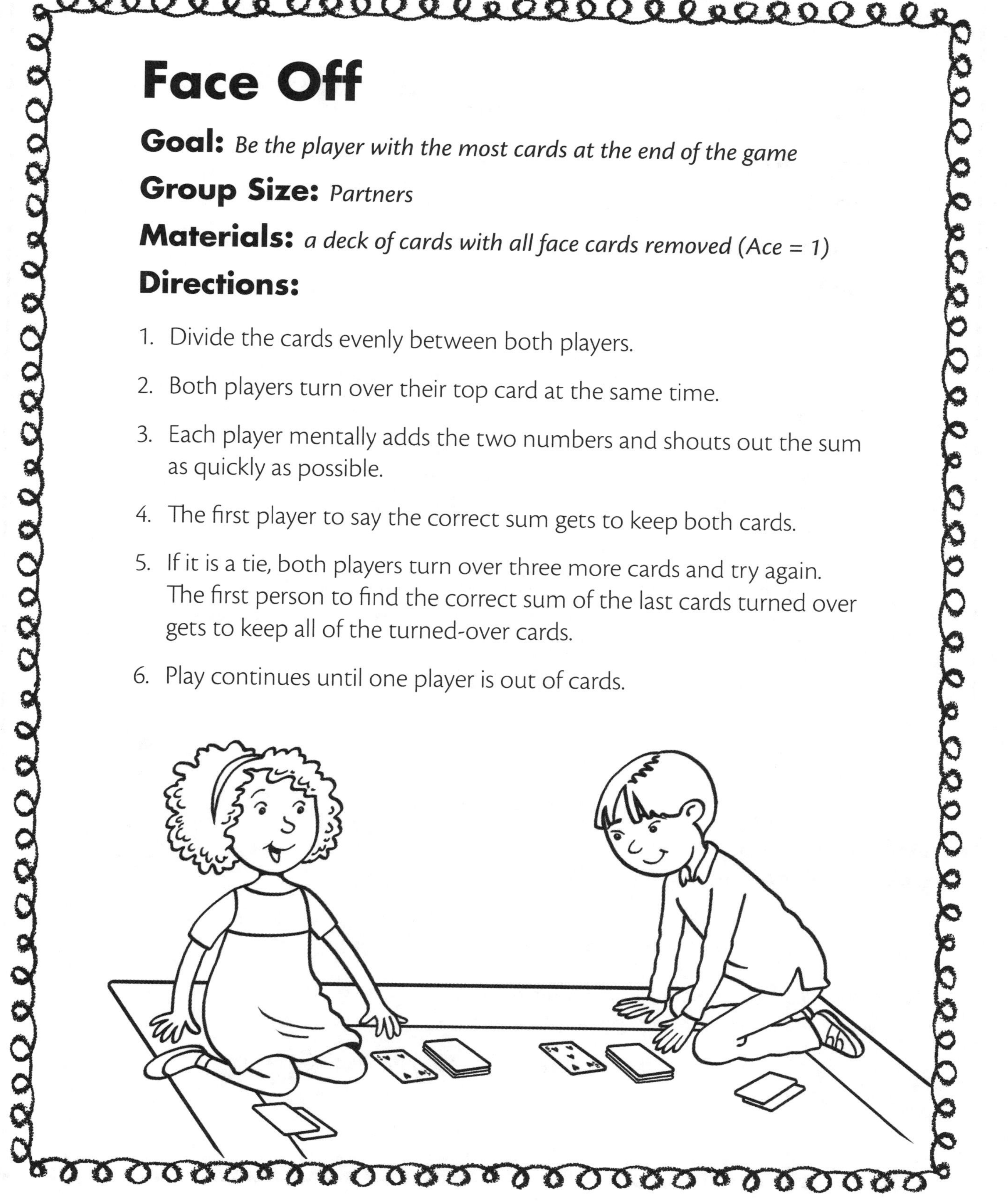

CPA: (A)

Target 10 and Target 55

Objective: *Practice addition facts and logical thinking*

Goal: *Be the first player to reach the target number*

Group Size: *Partners*

Materials: *game boards (see pages 150–151 for game board reproducibles) and counters*

Target 10 and Target 55 are fun and effective games (shared with us by our colleague Ricky Mikelman) that have a variety of possible outcomes. No two games are ever the same, yet purposeful cumulative addition remains constant. Target 10 allows for a scaffold into the more complex Target 55, where the total sum is determined by the two players. A reduced facsimile for including in the Practice side of the fluency folders is available on page 142.

Note: Provide both of these games as a reproducible stored inside a clear sheet for multiple uses. Students can either keep their game board in their Math Folder, or you can have a folder with all of the game boards accessible at any time. Taking this step will make it so you will not need to copy this game board more than once!

Switch It Up!

Here are some modifications you may wish to try:

- *The differentiation here comes somewhat from the gameboards themselves. Target 10 is for less proficient students; Target 55 is for more proficient students.*
- *To provide support, allow students to use a manipulative of their choice to model their choices and keep track of their target progression.*
- *Ask students to record each of their counter's progress toward the target number in number sentences.*

Target 10 and Target 55

Goal: *Be the first player to reach the target number*

Group Size: *Partners*

Materials: *game boards and counters*

Directions for Target 10:

1. Players take turns placing counters on the board as each tries to reach the target number 10.
2. Each time a player places a counter, that player must say the total of the numbers covered up to that point.
3. The first player to reach 10 exactly wins the game!

Directions for Target 55:

1. Both players agree on a target number between 25 and 55.
2. Players take turns placing counters on the board as each tries to reach the target number.
3. Each time a player places a counter, that player must say the total of the numbers he has covered.
4. The first player to reach the target number exactly wins the game!

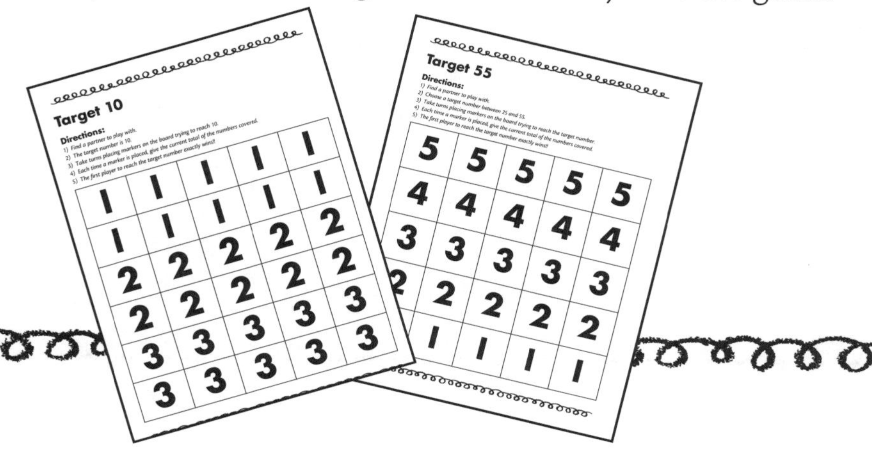

Game

CPA: (A)

Fast 10s

Objective: *Practice making combinations of 10*

Goal: *Earn the most points by the end of the game*

Group Size: *Partners*

Materials: *a deck of cards with all 10s and face cards removed (Ace = 1)*

By adding in a slight, yet subtle element of speed, Fast 10s can help students develop the automaticity we seek with their combinations to 10. Students are looking for two addends that make the sum of 10, but they must do this knowing they have a limited amount of time, and their opponent is waiting in the wings to find her own combinations. The opportunity to look before their turn, however, relieves some of the pressure. A reduced facsimile for including in the Practice side of the fluency folders is available on page 143.

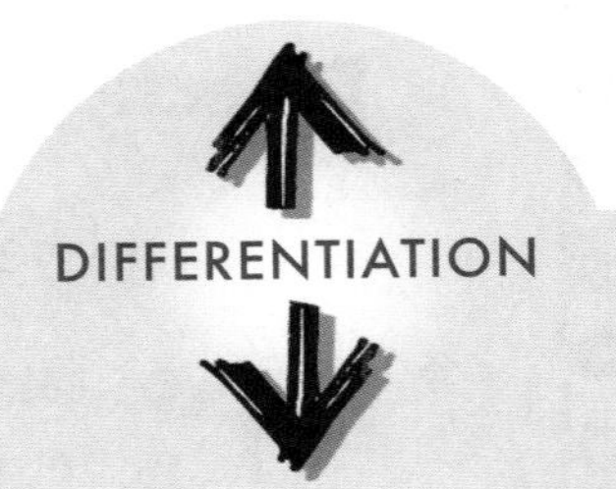

Switch It Up!

Here are some modifications you may wish to try:

- *Combine two decks of cards, but still use a 3 x 3 array layout, which allows for more than two addends to make a combination of 10.*
- *Record the number sentences for the combinations of 10. Look for patterns between total points and total matches.*

Fast 10s

Goal: *Earn the most points by the end of the game*

Group Size: *Partners*

Materials: *a deck of cards with all 10s and face cards removed (Ace = 1)*

Directions:

1. Player 1 shuffles the deck and places nine cards facing up in a 3 x 3 array (3 rows, 3 columns).
2. Player 2 looks for two cards that, when added together, make 10. Player 2 must find this pair of cards in about five seconds to keep the game moving. If he finds a pair, he takes the two cards and sets them in his side pile.
3. Player 2 now turns over two cards to fill in the empty spaces, and it's Player 1's turn to find two cards that make 10.
4. Players should be looking ahead to plan for pairs for when it is their turn.
5. If no two cards make 10, the player who could not make a pair may add a fourth row of three cards and try again.
6. Play continues until there are no cards left.
7. Players total their card point values. The person with the greatest value of cards (not necessarily most matches) is the winner.

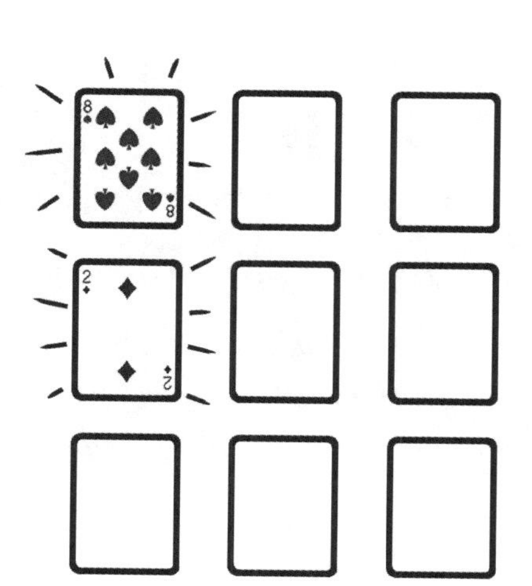

CPA: (A)

Countdown

Objective: *Practice addition and subtraction facts*

Goal: *Be the first player to turn over all of the numbers*

Group Size: *small groups, partners*

Materials: *index cards for the numbers 0–10 (one set per player), a pair of dice, paper and pencil for recording*

Countdown is a game that allows multiple opportunities for purposeful practice. Students are engaged because of the "gotcha" of rolling an 11 and making their opponents lose all progress and the "risk" of rolling a 12 and having to turn over their own numbers. Countdown is a true gem—a low-prep, high-yield game. A reduced facsimile for including in the Practice side of the fluency folders is available on page 143.

Note: You don't have to use index cards for the numbers in this game. You could use paper tiles, the cards from a deck of cards (using Queen for 0), or even numbers written on pieces of paper.

Switch It Up!

Here are some modifications you may wish to try:

- *For an extra challenge, you can throw in the operations of multiplication and division.*
- *For an extra-*extra *challenge, you can add a third die to the mix and use all four operations; students can use one, two, or three of the dice on any turn, as well as any operation—addition, subtraction, multiplication, and division.*

Countdown

Goal: *Be the first player to turn over all of the numbers*

Group Size: *Small groups, partners*

Materials: *index cards for the numbers 0–10 (one set per player), a pair of dice, paper and pencil for recording*

Directions:

1. All players lay out their number cards 0–10 in order, face up.
2. The first player rolls the dice and either adds or subtracts to find a sum or difference that is shown on one of the cards.
3. If the roll is between 0–10, the player turns over or crosses off that number. For example, if the sum or difference (whichever operation is being used for that round) of the roll was 3, the player that rolled turns over his or her 3 card.
4. The player who rolled records the number sentence used to get the sum or difference.
5. If the roll is a 5 and a 6, it can only be used as an 11. When an 11 is rolled, the other player(s) must return any of their turned-over numbers back to their number side. The player who rolled is "safe."
6. If the roll is 12, that means the person rolling has to turn over her own cards to their original positions, and the other players are "safe."
7. If no number sentence will work, the player loses his turn, and it is the next player's turn.

Players keep taking turns until there are no cards or numbers left to turn over.

CPA: (A)

Bonds to 10

Objective: *Develop fluency with bonds to 10*

Goal: *Make bonds of 10 and then guess the Mystery Card*

Group Size: *Whole class, small groups, partners, individual*

Materials: *a deck of cards with all face cards removed (Ace = 1)*

This game gives students practice making bonds to 10. Whether played individually, with a partner or small group, or as a whole class, the process of making bonds of 10 solidifies understanding and, with practice, helps students improve their personal adding time. The game directions are reproducible so students can play independently. A reduced facsimile for including in the Practice side of the fluency folders is available on page 144.

Note: Have students create a visual representation of a game to help them make sense of and memorize the rules.

DIFFERENTIATION

Switch It Up!

Here are some differentiation ideas for this game:

- *Consider working for speed. Once the deck is ready, time how long it takes students to find the Mystery Card. Students don't need to race against each other but rather make steady improvements on their own time.*
- *Try having students graph their times (using a grade-appropriate graph).*
- *Allow providing manipulatives such as 10-frames, rekenreks, or other 10-creating support.*
- *Try having students play in partners so one person can say the bonds and one person can check the bonds.*
- *Consider playing with bonds to 5. Here are a few modifications you'll need to make to play this way:*
  - *Remove all cards greater than 5.*
  - *Keep the face cards, which will become 5.*
  - *Play as per usual with bonds to 5 instead of bonds to 10.*

Bonds to 10

Goal: *Make bonds of 10 and then guess the Mystery Card*

Group Size: *Whole class, small groups, partners, individual*

Materials: *a deck of cards with all face cards removed (Ace = 1)*

Directions:

1. Pull one card. Do not look at it. This will be your Mystery Card. Set this card aside.
2. Deal out 11 cards face up.
3. If there are any 10s, cover them with a new card (face up) from the deck because 10 + 0 = 10.
4. Now, look for two cards that are face up and equal 10 when added together. For example, 5 + 5 = 10 or A (1) + 9 = 10. Cover those cards with new cards from the deck. These new cards should also be facing up.
5. Continue to cover 10s with new cards from the deck until the deck is gone.
6. If you are left with a 10 in your deck, set it aside.
7. Look at the piles on the desk. Find two piles whose top cards make 10 when added together. For example, a pile with an 8 on top can be put with a pile with a 2 on top. Continue until only one pile is left.
8. That pile and your Mystery Card should equal 10! Can you guess what your Mystery Card is before flipping it over?

CPA: (C)

Bullwinkle

Objective: *Compose and decompose numbers; visualize numbers*

Goal: *Practice composing and decomposing numbers*

Group Size: *Whole class, partners*

Materials: *Fingers!*

Bullwinkle is an activity that can be used throughout the math block as a great formative assessment tool. It allows the teacher to be able to see all students' thinking to a given question instead of calling on only one student for an answer.

Directions: Students use their hands as "antlers" (like Bullwinkle the moose!) above their heads where they cannot see their hands. This forces them to visualize the numbers their hands are making to create the numbers you provide them with.

Suggested prompts:

Ways to make numbers less than 10: Students, working alone, show numbers based on teacher's directions.

For example:

- Can you make 6 using two hands?
- Is there another way?
- Another way?
- Can you make 8 using two hands?

Ways to make numbers less than 10 with a partner: Students must make a number (called by the teacher) that is different than their partner.

Ways to make 10: The teacher shows a number (part) and students must show the missing part to create 10 (the whole).

Ways to make numbers greater than 10 (partners): Students, facing each other, must make the number given.

For example:

- Can you make 14? (Note: Each student must give the parts to make the whole by adjusting together without talking.)
- Can you make 17?

Ways to make numbers to 10 or greater than 10 (three students): Students, facing each other, must make the number given using all three students' "antlers" without talking.

For example:

- Can you make 15? (Based on what the three students show, they must problem-solve to adjust to make the given number without talking.)
- Can you make 23?

Ways to make numbers greater than 1.0, when each finger is 0.1: Students use their fingers, and each finger equals 0.1.

For example:

- Can you make 0.8? (For individual students)
- Can you make 1.4? (For partners, as one student can only make 1.0)

PART 3: All about Multiplication and Division

PART 3: All about Multiplication and Division

Teaching for Understanding

concrete (adj):

using hands-on manipulatives to deliver math instruction conceptually (i.e., teddy bear counters, base-10 blocks, bean sticks, etc.)

pictorial (adj):

representing numbers, equations, or word problems with pictures or other visual representations (i.e., drawn pictures of items, model drawing, bar models, tape diagrams, strip diagrams, etc.)

abstract (adj):

the final stage in the math continuum where students demonstrate an understanding of the process by solving the problem with an algorithm

When we first started teaching, we hadn't looked at multiplication and division facts as anything other than something to be memorized and used because that's how we'd been taught. Make no mistake—memorization is still one important piece of the mathematical puzzle. However, there is so much more to the puzzle as a whole. As educators today, we have many tools, and we must use them to support students' success (through teaching) versus supporting anxiety-ridden practices (through isolated, unconnected timed tests and drills).

To teach students what multiplication and division are, we need to help students recognize the patterns contained within the two operations. We need to begin with the basics, just like we did for addition and subtraction. We need to take our teaching and the opportunity for learning back to the **concrete**, back to the manipulation of the operations.

It's important that students learn and understand the uniqueness of these two new operations and see how they relate to addition and subtraction. For example, multiplication can be viewed as repeated addition, and division can be viewed as repeated subtraction. Students also need to see how the operations also have their own unique properties (i.e., addition and multiplication can use the Associative Property, while subtraction and division cannot).

Again, rather than resorting to timed tests, we will guide students to move from the concrete to the **pictorial**, to the **abstract**, and then lead them to fluency through purposeful practice.

Hula Hoop Math

We have found that the best way to begin is with large activities to develop the concept of multiplying or dividing a number. Take students out to a large space, such as the playground, and have them organize themselves into hula hoop groups.

For example:

- To show 3 x 2 (could be said as three groups of two), you need three hula hoops and two students to plant themselves in each hoop. How many students in all?
- To show the Commutative Property of Multiplication, have the same six students use only two hula hoops. Students will see how the product remains the same, but the way the problem looks is different. This difference in appearance is very important when they apply their understanding in number stories (aka word problems).
- Conversely, when students are ready for division, demonstrate how the six students can be divided by three hula hoops by having two of them step inside each one. As there would not be any students outside a hula hoop, you could show that there were no leftovers, or remainders, and therefore the number evenly divides.
- Repeat this activity when you are ready to introduce the concept of remainders. Have seven students divide into two hula hoops.

While some of your students are modeling the problem, other students can record what is being demonstrated with the hula hoops. For example, they could draw a picture of the students in hula hoops, they could show 2 + 2 + 2, or they could write the equation as presented with the answer, i.e., 3 x 2 = 6.

Kinesthetic activities like this are fun, effective ways to add energy and life to your instruction. They shake things up, help students burn off energy, and deepen understanding in a visual, concrete and memorable way.

As these different representations emerge, try to make connections to students' previous understandings and give them hints as to what will follow.

Using the C-P-A Approach

Once the large, gross-motor activity has been concluded, you're ready for more concrete experiences, but on a smaller scale.

By teaching multiplication facts using a concrete-pictorial-abstract (C-P-A) approach, students will develop a solid foundation for fact fluency. They can see these facts as their individual parts ***and*** as a whole, or in other words—a memorized, fluent fact. They'll know that 6 x 6 has an answer of 36, but they will also know that the product can also be created using the parts in different ways. Students will begin to see patterns and pictures within the facts. They will be able to see that a 6 x 6 problem looks like a square, which will lead them to understand it as 6 groups of 6. They will understand that the fact could also be 5 x 6 and 1 x 6 combined to make 6 x 6. Students will be able to use their newly developed understandings to create mental math strategies.

Helpful Hint! *Before working with manipulatives of any sort, always allow students the opportunity to "play" with the manipulatives before asking them to use them as a tool. Making a T chart to define what students can do with manipulatives when they're toys versus what they can do with them when they're tools is super helpful. Label one side of the T chart, "What it looks like" and label the other half, "What it sounds like."*

To fill in the chart, pass out manipulatives and ask your students to use them as if they were toys. Give them about five minutes. Then, bring students back together and have them brainstorm what kinds of things an observer would have seen if they had walked into the room during the activity. The images they describe (e.g., a tower, a spaceship, a boat) should be drawn or described in the "What it looks like" side of the chart. Then have students list the different sounds the observer might have heard as the students used the manipulatives as toys (e.g., lots of noise, talking about movies, strange sounds). List these sounds under "What it sounds like."

Repeat this activity to fill out the flip side of the chart, only this time ask your students to use the manipulatives as math tools. Repeat the discussion about what you should see and hear when you're working with math tools. Now, whenever students are using manipulatives, you simply display the appropriate side of the chart. This will remind students how to use the manipulatives and ensure good student behavior.

TOYS

Looks Like	Sounds Like
• exploring • alone • with friends • creative designs • messy • stacking and falling	• noise level 2 and higher • laughter • sound effects • social talk

TOOLS

Looks Like	Sounds Like
• strategic choices • independent • with partners • math planning • problem solving • messy, but precise and organized	• noise level 2 and lower • conversation • questions • math talk • respectful critique and argument

A Suggested Order for Teaching Multiplication

We suggest that you use the following sequence to teach multiplication facts: 10, 5, 2, 4, 8, 3, 6, 9, and then 7. When facts are purposefully broken down or sequenced into groups of understanding, students begin to use what they know about one set of facts to learn the next set. For example, students will use what they know about their 10s facts to make sense of their 5s facts. It is a natural scaffolding built in to the sequence!

Starting with 10 and 5

Why do we start with 10? Most teaching of multiplication follows teaching in place value. During the instruction of place-value units, students learn how to build groups of 10. For example, they learn that 5 groups (or bundles) of 10 has a value of 50. They continue this progression up to learning that 12 groups of 10 has a value of 120. This is a great concept to use as a springboard into understanding multiplication. Once students are comfortable with understanding the 10s facts, we use that information to move into learning and understanding 5. The two sets of facts naturally fit together.

Here is an example of a conversation you may find yourself having with a student one day:

You: ***If you know 10 x 10 = 100, what do you notice with 5 x 10 = 50?***

Student: ***Oh! Multiplying by 5 is half of multiplying by 10!***

Students' understanding of the 10s facts paves the way for more of those "Ah-ha!" moments such as this.

As you guide students to understand this connection, they will understand multiplying by 5 at a deeper level than just knowing that, "When you multiply a whole number by 5, the product ends in either a 0 or 5." While it is true—products of 5 end in either 0 or 5, you can help students go deeper in their understanding by taking this a step further and looking at the products of their 5s.

Some questions you could use are:

- Is there a pattern you see?
- What do you notice about all of the products that end in 5?
- Is there something similar about the other factor?

By teaching multiplication to this depth, students will walk away with a clearer understanding of the ***meaning*** behind the facts than they would if they had just learned them by rote memorization. They'll know from their own experience that a whole number multiplied by 5 ends in a 5 or a 0, or that in order for a whole number to be divisible by 5, the number must end in a 5 or a 0. Moving forward, when they get stuck on a fact, they will have reasoning to fall back on to help them figure out the answer.

Moving Beyond 10 and 5

Once 10s and 5s facts are understood, lead students into an understanding of 2s, 4s, and 8s. You could say, "If you know your 2s, you also know your 4s because 4s are a double, and 8s are a double of the double." We want students to continue to look for patterns. Once again, have them look at the products and guide them with prompts or questions.

Some prompts you could use are:

- Do you see any other patterns?
- Do you see any odd products?
- If we are multiplying a whole number by 2, 4, or 8, could the product be 37? Why or why not?

This deeper understanding is going to take students' knowledge of multiplication to the next level. It will also help when discovering divisibility rules. In our past, divisibility rules were something we handed out in a chart. Now, the kids will own those divisibility rules. They'll be a tool they always have, not something they have to dig to find in their desk.

We can continue this thinking and process with 3s and 6s (6 is a double of 3), and 9s. Nine facts are often known because of the finger tricks that may have been passed down from generation to generation, but we can show 9 as a 3 fact plus a 6 fact, and it can also be shown as one group less than a 10 fact.

The Brain as a Pattern Detector

This is a perfect time to compare patterns from previously learned facts. Ask your class: *How can we use previous understanding to help us learn these facts?* Students love to look for patterns. We promise you that once you allow your students to start unlocking and exploring patterns, they will become pattern detectives, and their learning won't stop! They will gain momentum with learning their facts because of the deeper knowledge level you will have tapped into. This will take them much further than just rote memorization in isolation!

Sevens and the Distributive Property

Finally, we will finish up with 7. Here we can think about any 7 fact as being a 5 fact plus a 2 fact. For example, 7 x 6 is like thinking about 5 x 6 plus 2 x 6. And here's a bonus: By introducing 7 in this manner, you are also exposing your students to the Distributive Property! The Distributive Property is typically a hard property to teach students because traditionally, we wait until we reach two- and three-digit numbers. But waiting that long causes us to miss a golden opportunity for understanding. By introducing this property early with our basic facts, students are more likely to understand it and see the value behind it for mental math. But keep it simple!

Here is a fun activity you can use to help students understand the Distributive Property. All you'll need are numbered index cards and students who are ready to learn.

1. Have two students stand. Give each student a number card, such as 7 and 8.
2. Then, decompose 7 by inviting a third student up.
3. Take back the 7 card, and hand that student a 2 card. Then hand the new student a 5 card. So the three students are holding cards 2, 5, and 8.
4. Have the student holding the 8 card "distribute" to the 5 and multiply to get 40 (8 x 5 = 40). Ask students to hold that number in their minds.
5. Then have the 8 distribute to the 2 to get 16 (8 x 2 = 16).
6. Add 40 and 16 together to get 56, which is also the answer to 7 x 8!

To solidify the activity, you could also have your students record the process as it is shown here:

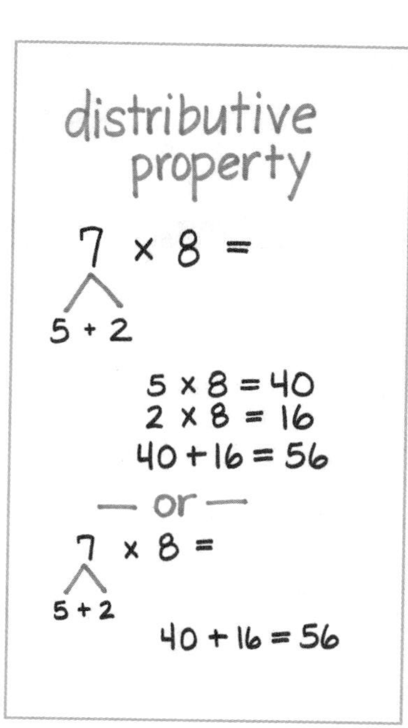

As you model this process, do one or both recordings simultaneously to show the connections between the actions and the algorithms. Keep in mind that some of your sports enthusiasts will know some of their early 7 facts by thinking about touchdowns and extra points!

Words of Encouragement

Please know that this is not a quick process, and we understand that, at times, you may feel the urge to cut corners to speed things up a bit. You may also have people asking why are you making it so tedious and not just telling them 7 x 8 = 56. Your answer is we are TEACHING them their facts so they can memorize them. However, if they understand the number sense behind the facts, they can always reason their way through a problem if they've forgotten the fact they once thought they had memorized. But we promise you—taking the extra time to truly teach, to help your students become fluent in their math skills, is worth it! Remember: **Move slow now, so you can move fast later.**

The Six-Page Journal

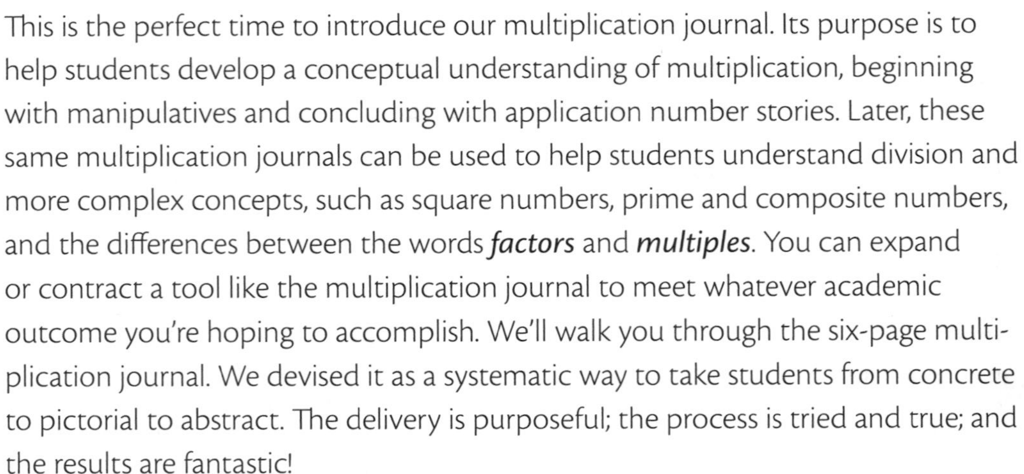

This is the perfect time to introduce our multiplication journal. Its purpose is to help students develop a conceptual understanding of multiplication, beginning with manipulatives and concluding with application number stories. Later, these same multiplication journals can be used to help students understand division and more complex concepts, such as square numbers, prime and composite numbers, and the differences between the words ***factors*** and ***multiples***. You can expand or contract a tool like the multiplication journal to meet whatever academic outcome you're hoping to accomplish. We'll walk you through the six-page multiplication journal. We devised it as a systematic way to take students from concrete to pictorial to abstract. The delivery is purposeful; the process is tried and true; and the results are fantastic!

The multiplication journal can be used as the teaching tool for the grade level that expects students to have their math facts from memory (in many states, this is the 3rd grade), or as the intervention tool for those students who need to be retaught properly (4th grade and higher). It can also be passed on to succeeding grade levels to teach higher-level concepts of multiplication, connecting the previous grade level's work to new, more complex concepts.

These directions are written using the example of 10 as our teaching factor. However, you will go through this six-page layout or sequence for each factor. This process is time-consuming, but that's also what makes it effective for teaching students at a level of depth they need.

Helpful Hint! *Before beginning, a word of warning for those choosing to have each student create their own journal: Providing loose pages of paper as you go offers up an opportunity for the disorganized to become even more disorganized. The build-up, or sequence, is part of the process, so take the time to prep ahead of class to make success a natural outcome for all of your students.*

Pages 1 and 2: Patterns in Multiplication, Multiplication Equations

1. Place your students into groups of about four. Hand out manipulatives (i.e., connecting cubes, beans, etc.) to each group and explain that they will be using the manipulatives to make equal groups.
2. Begin by asking: ***How many equal groups of 10 has your group made?*** or ***How many counters have you used?*** As no groups of 10 have been made yet, the answer will be "0."
3. All students should color in "0" on the hundreds board that is page 1 of the student's journal. Then, students should record 0 x 10 = 0 on page 2. As students are recording the equation, talk about how to read the equation. Explain that it should be read "0 groups of 10 equals 0." By using the words ***groups of*** instead of ***times*** you are helping students create a more visual picture in their minds.
4. Now tell each group to make one group of 10 with their manipulatives. Discuss how many equal groups they now see. Ask: ***How many total manipulatives have you used?***

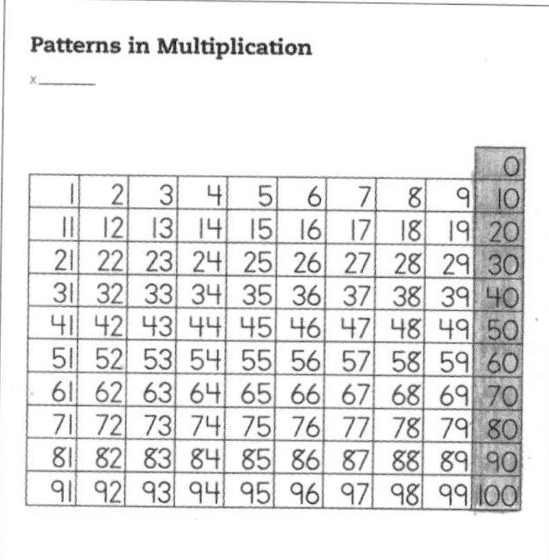

Patterns in Multiplication

x_____

									0
1	2	3	4	5	6	7	8	9	10
11	12	13	14	15	16	17	18	19	20
21	22	23	24	25	26	27	28	29	30
31	32	33	34	35	36	37	38	39	40
41	42	43	44	45	46	47	48	49	50
51	52	53	54	55	56	57	58	59	60
61	62	63	64	65	66	67	68	69	70
71	72	73	74	75	76	77	78	79	80
81	82	83	84	85	86	87	88	89	90
91	92	93	94	95	96	97	98	99	100

5. On the hundreds board, each student should color in the total number of counters used. On page 2, record the equation 1 x 10 = 10.
6. Ask students to read the equation they just wrote. Again, when they read it, have them use the words ***groups of*** instead of ***times***. This will help them visualize the groups they just created with the counters. It will also help them when they work with arrays, and, later on, with division when they're asked to either share equally or repeatedly subtract.
7. Repeat steps 4 through 6 until the hundreds board is complete. The idea throughout this activity is to let students discover their own patterns. Stop frequently to ask what patterns they're noticing. Avoid giving students quick fixes or shortcuts. Use the multiplication patterns that were previously discussed as your guide to help students unlock these patterns. There is enough space at the bottom of the hundreds chart for students to respond about what patterns they're noticing.

Pages 3 and 4: Two Pages of Area Models

Before we dive into these two pages, we want to take a moment and discuss the difference between arrays and area models. These two representations are sometimes confused, and it's important that the differences are understood moving forward.

Most of us are very comfortable having our students make arrays, or visual representations of multiplication, using manipulatives or drawing on paper. However, it is important to keep in mind that the items or objects in arrays are not connected.

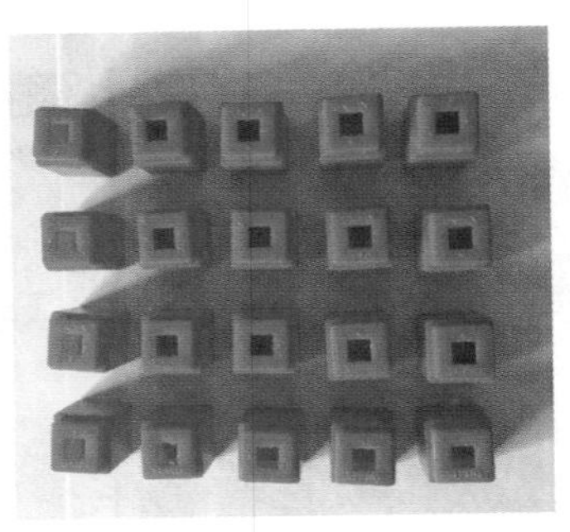

An example of a 4 x 5 array made with manipulatives

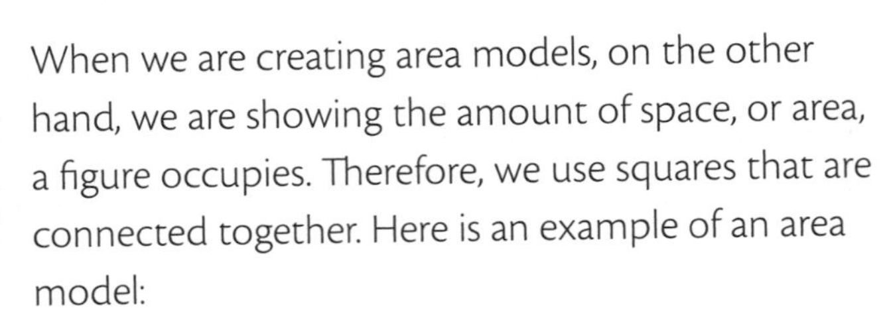

When we are creating area models, on the other hand, we are showing the amount of space, or area, a figure occupies. Therefore, we use squares that are connected together. Here is an example of an area model:

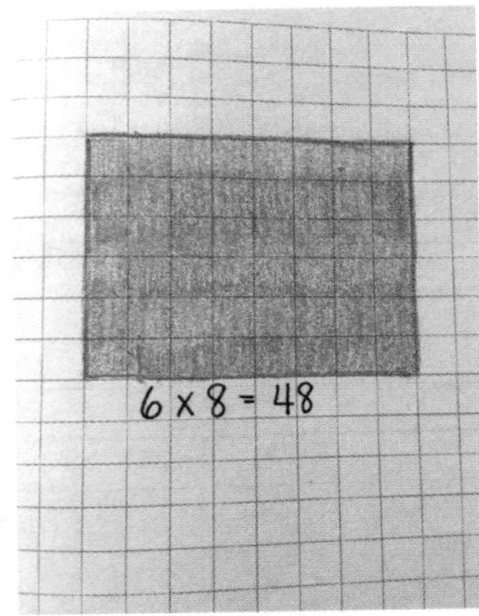

An example of a 6 x 8 area model drawn on graph paper

Teachers typically teach area models as a strategy for multi-digit multiplication. But by introducing and using this strategy with basic facts, students typically have a better understanding of how to use the strategy when they need to use it to solve more complex problems.

As you create these next two pages with your students, talk about what the term ***area*** means. More often than not, ***area*** is taught at the same time as ***perimeter***; students have a very difficult time distinguishing the differences between them. They know that both terms connect to measurement and geometry, but they can't remember which formula to use for each. Here, the visuals your students create will help drive home the reason we multiply to find area. As they create the images on graph paper, they will see the "square units." This visual representation will remind students in the future that, when giving an answer to a problem asking about area, it needs to be labeled in terms of square units.

Students will use these pages to create area models for their equations.

1. Have students begin by coloring in an area for 1 x 10. Remember to discuss that this is one group of 10, and that the length is 1 unit and the width is 10 units.

2. Once the area is colored in, record the equation underneath the model. For example: 1 x 10 = 10. If you want to reinforce the area concept, have students record it like this: 1 unit x 10 units = 10 square units.
3. Have students turn their journal sideways. Now they can see how the problem looks from a different perspective. Now we see 10 groups of 1 unit. Have students record this equation under the new image: 10 x 1 = 10, or 10 units x 1 unit = 10 square units. Use the visual and equations to illustrate and teach the Commutative Property of Multiplication. Yes, the product is the same, but the way the problems look is different. As mentioned earlier, this is a very important concept to stress.
4. Repeat steps 1 through 3 for area models up through 10 groups.
5. Once students are finished, have them look at the visual diagrams they just completed. What do they notice? You may have a student who says, "I notice that only one is a square and the rest are rectangles." This kind of an observation presents you and your students with a wonderful "I wonder" opportunity, which are opportunities in which students are allowed the time to explore certain things they notice. Don't jump in and tell your class why there is only one square area on the page. Instead, respond with something along the lines of, "I wonder why that is. I wonder if when we do more area models, will they also have only one square? I wonder if there is a reason why there is only one square."

Helpful Hint! *Teach students the difference between rows and columns. This is a life skill they can apply again and again. One way to do this is to draw a picture or nonlinguistic representation to support their understanding. Here is just one example.*

Once you have completed your journals, come back to this idea. Have students look on the pages with their area models, and on a separate piece of paper or dry-erase board, record all of the equations that created a square area. Ask students: ***What do you notice?*** This prompt is the perfect segue into a great conversation regarding square numbers. The children's book ***My Full Moon*** by Elinor Pinczes ties in perfectly with this discussion.

If you have the space, create an "I Wonder" bulletin board in your classroom. Every time a student arrives at an "I wonder" moment, have him record the "I wonder" thought on a card and tack it to the board. This board allows you to recognize students' questions and reminds them that, as a class, you will continue to look for the answers or reasons as you continue to work.

Page 5: Real-World Connection Story

The purpose of this page is to make the connection to the real world, the students' world. It is important to let students use topics that are relevant and meaningful to them! This is not a whole-class direct instruction process where everyone draws basketballs. Students choose their meaning and their content for their multiplication representation.

1. Students should create a visual representation for their problem. For example, it can be a basic picture that mirrors the story; a bar model or tape diagram; or an array or area model. You could challenge students to show their thinking using one or more of these suggestions. Please note that most states ask that students show answers in more than one way.
2. Students should record the correct equation that matches the problem.
3. Students should provide a number sentence that correctly answers the question.

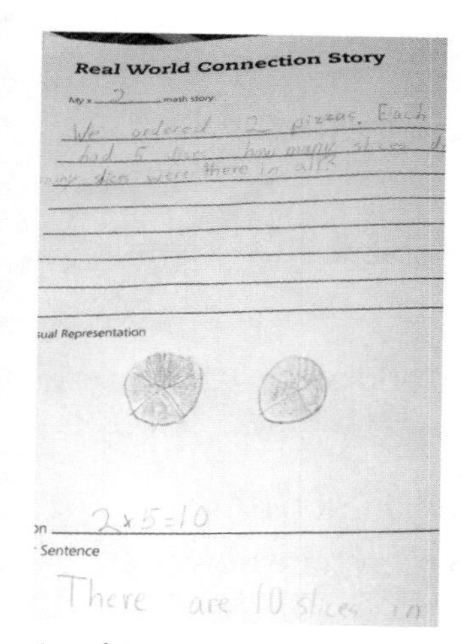

Level 1

Level 2

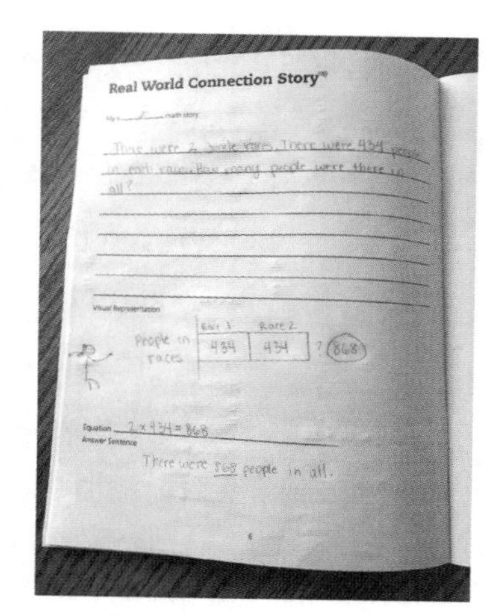

Level 3

Help students decide which level of understanding applies to them:

Level 1—basic knowledge level of multiplying by 10; write a real-world story problem multiplying 10 by numbers from 1 through 10.

Level 2—solid knowledge of multiplying by 10; write a real-world story problem multiplying 10 by numbers from 11 through 99.

Level 3—challenge level; write a real-world story problem multiplying 10 by a three- or four-digit number.

Page 6: Extension

The final page in the sequence is for extensions to the multiplication instruction (i.e., the math facts, strategies for multiplication, patterns they've observed, etc.) students have now had. This could be a math station, a small-group opportunity or assignment, or something you choose to match your class's needs.

You could have your students:

- Write a how-to paragraph about multiplication
- Write/illustrate additional multiplication and/or division real-world stories
- Plan, write, and illustrate a multiplication story using a favorite children's book
- Play a favorite game with a younger buddy from a class in a lower grade
- Design an anchor chart for their classmates that can later be enlarged for whole-class use
- Create their own extension

As a teacher you could:

- Teach a game and have students record directions in a jotted or sketch-noted format
- Teach the Distributive Property and have students practice decomposing the numbers
- Compare and contrast multiplication and repeated addition, such as how they are similar and how they are different
- Explain the connection between multiplication and division (take a number that students are working on and then demonstrate how this relates to division)
- Challenge students to create their own extension

Throughout the process, consider asking questions of your students such as:

- Why are you correct?
- What do you see?
- What relationship do you notice between the factors (for example, between 2, 4, and 8)?
- Is there another way?
- Can you show me?

We want to create lifelong learners who go the extra mile. The point of all these extension suggestions is to show you that there's so much more you can do and that instructional ideas are endless. We have provided you with just a few suggestions to help you create those lifelong learners and encourage your students to continuously extend themselves even when you're not around guiding and encouraging them.

Helpful Hint! *It's very important that we do not give students the concept of just adding a 0 when multiplying by 10 or 00 when multiplying by a 100 or even 000 when multiplying by 1,000. This works fine for whole numbers. However, this will fall apart for them later on when they try and generalize and apply the quick fix to decimals. For example, simply adding the 0 from the 10 will not work here. We only want to help students create accurate generalizations, not quick fixes that may not hold up over time.*

Anchor Charts

As students develop their understanding of multiplication, an anchor chart could again be created that shows all the ways we can think about multiplication. These charts would be specific to your classroom instruction and your expectations for teaching.

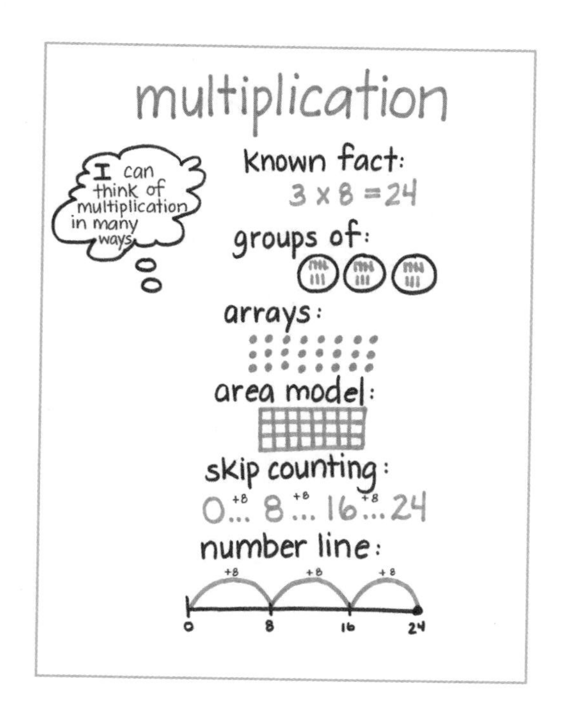

Some teachers find that teaching more than one strategy at a time can be confusing to students; they prefer to add strategies to the anchor chart as they are taught throughout the unit. Other teachers like to give students all of the options at once and have them use those that are most effective for them as learners.

A multiplication anchor chart might include these concepts:

- Repeated addition
- Groups of
- Arrays
- Area (length x width)
- Skip counting on a number line
- Known facts

Helpful Hint! *Try not to create a chart ahead of time. Allow the chart to develop as students' understanding and strategies develop. A chart that is made as a class establishes increased buy-in because it is not a chart that was merely purchased, but rather it is something created by the students themselves.*

As students recognize patterns from their work with the six-page journal and from creating anchor charts, they will come to the natural conclusion about the various properties that exist. They will have experience with them. They will have seen them work before their very own eyes.

Self-Generated Resources

In the past, we taught mathematical words and properties in isolation, often only as vocabulary words. Can anyone else relate? However, it is imperative that students see these properties (such as the Identity Property of Zero, the Identity Property of One, the Commutative Property, the Distributive Property, and Associative Property of Multiplication) not as mere words, but as strategies—something they and other mathematicians can rely on to help solve problems.

As you teach the various properties, it can be useful to have students create their own reference materials, something they can use when solving problems ranging from simple math facts to more complex applications. When students have their own, self-generated resources, they see themselves as the driver of their own math learning. They also can demonstrate to you that they can choose the appropriate tool (in this case, their notes or reference materials) and use them strategically and appropriately. If using references becomes a part of students' daily instruction, it will become a natural and permanent part of their mathematical routine.

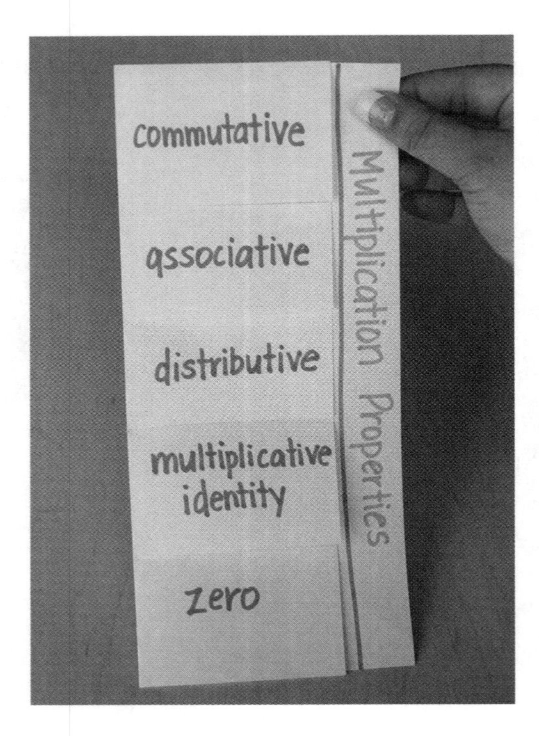

Here is an example of a foldable we've used and found to be very helpful.

A Foldable

One way to create the habit of choosing and using the appropriate resources is to create a foldable with different tabs for the different properties. As students recognize different mathematical properties add them to their foldable.

On the outside of the tab, record the name of the property. We've recorded the Commutative Property on the first tab on our foldable. Open the tab. On the inside of the tab, students should write a definition for the property in their own words. On the space on the other side, students should record an example of the property.

Students being allowed the time to make sense of their understanding, one property at a time, one day at a time, is much more powerful than that same time being used for a timed test. The foldable can be used as an assessment tool as well. At the end of instruction, tell the students which properties they need to explain and show.

Moving Toward Automaticity

Now that students have a sense of what multiplication is, what it looks like, how it's written, what properties work with the operation of multiplication, and how it applies to the world around them, we can move into that purposeful practice to develop automaticity.

When thinking about automaticity with multiplication and division facts, it's important to remember that this will develop over time. In the previous section, we looked at how to develop an understanding of what multiplication and division means, and now we'll take the next step.

Just as we discussed with addition and subtraction, we're suggesting you help students develop automaticity through purposeful practice. You've got a lot of ideas of your own that you can fit into your schedule to support students, and we're going to give you even more.

Fluency Folders

As stated in Part 2, fluency folders are a powerful tool for your students to use and are often used on a daily basis. We've found this resource is an enormous aid in helping students set personal goals, practice their understanding at a rate appropriate to their grade level and their learning style, have their progress assessed individually, and then celebrate as they make progress closer and closer to their goal. Finally, students get the chance to play games to practice and to celebrate at a speed that works for them. This purposeful game-playing allows for the efficiency component of fluency to develop and for those facts to be committed to memory.

We have outlined the directions to make a fluency folder on pages 40–41 in Part 2. While the process to make the folders will be the same as when making the folders for addition and subtraction, the charts attached to each section will now relate to multiplication and division facts.

Some teachers have found it beneficial to copy the multiplication facts on the piece of paper that will become the folded half-sized portrait sheet of paper, so the chart is on the front (for a pre-assessment) and on the back (for the on-going assessment leading to a celebration of all facts known from memory).

Once students have created their folders, they can decide which math facts they need to practice. Our students are oftentimes their own most brutal critics. If you've been developing them as mathematical thinkers and created that safe classroom, they'll have a very good idea about which facts they know efficiently and automatically and which facts are still giving them trouble.

What you'll find is that there's a small section of facts students struggle with. In fact, you probably already knew this. But that is okay. Students will cruise through much of the sequence, and then they can focus on the "toughies," such as the 6s, 7s, and 8s. But, with all the instruction you've done and the strategies students now own, they'll get these in time, too.

Practice Cards

To help students master the facts, have them create cards for one set of facts to practice until they are fluent. Remember how sight words are taught to students when they're beginning readers? This is a similar approach. Students will work in small, digestible chunks. Don't give them 100 facts to work on all at once. Rather, just give them a few, a few that they can concentrate on—a few that they have previous understanding of from all the work they've already done.

The front side of the practice card should be a traditional math fact (i.e., 7 x 4). The back side should be a pictorial representation of this math fact (i.e., seven groups of four items, or a 7 x 4 array, or 7 x 2 plus 7 x 2). The back should also include the answer. While working with students, you'll find it very helpful to emphasize strategies such as Double Double for 8s and using the Distributive Property for 7 by breaking it into 5 and 2. Students don't often think of strategies when they're trying to memorize. But by thinking back on the strategies, figuring out the answer after some work, and having repeated exposure, they'll start to hold the facts in their memory!

Helpful Hint! *What is Double Double? Double Double is a strategy to teach your students when they are working on their 8 facts. Begin by having students look for the pattern or relationship between 2, 4, and 8. Ask: What do you notice about these numbers? We hope they will recognize that 4 is double 2, and 8 is double 4. Once the pattern is understood, call out some facts for students to record on dry-erase boards. For example, call out 2 x 6 followed by 4 x 6, then 2 x 10 followed by 4 x 10, and then 2 x 5 followed by 4 x 5. Guide students to discover the patterns in the products as shown below:*

2 x 6 = 12	2 x 10 = 20	2 x 5 = 10
4 x 6 = 24	4 x 10 = 40	4 x 5 = 20

Once students recognize that the product doubles when the first factor doubles, have them record the 8 fact in each column:

8 x 6 = 48	8 x 10 = 80	8 x 5 = 40

Again, have students look at the products. Can they detect that multiplying by 8 is yet another double? You double the 2 fact once to get the 4 fact, and double it again to get the 8 fact! Double Double! Once your students catch on to this with basic facts, try it with two- and three-digit numbers as well.

Flash Facts Cards

For students who already have the conceptual understanding or are already showing efficiency with their math facts, flash facts cards with multiplication facts on one side and the answers and division practice on the other are an effective and engaging option for practice.

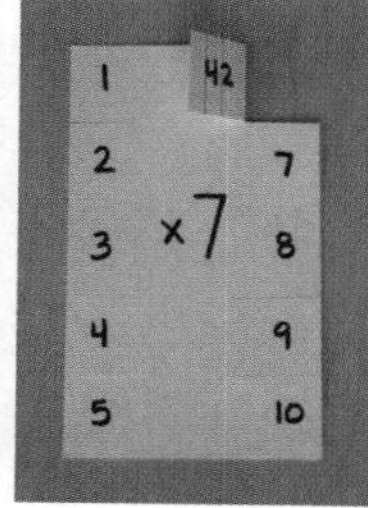

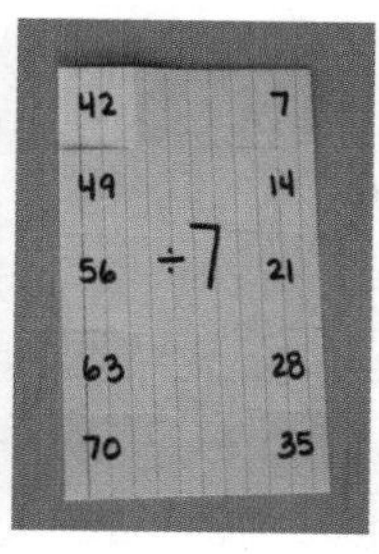

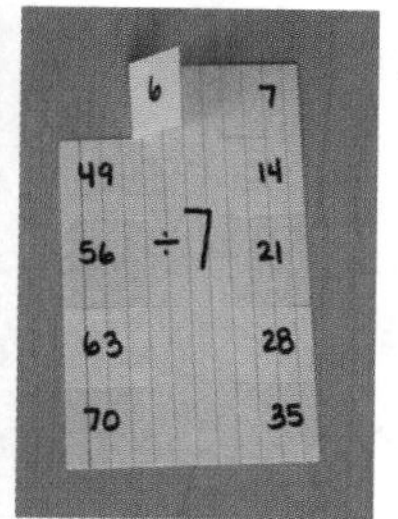

Students can practice their facts until they believe they are fluent (fluency = understanding + accuracy + efficiency). They can use the flash facts cards by themselves, or with a partner because they are self-checking. A variety of practice activities will ensure your students stay engaged and have fun.

Assessment Time

When students believe they're ready to be assessed, they should move their practice cards or the flash fact cards over to the Assess part of their folder. By conducting an oral one-on-one assessment with the student, you have the opportunity to ask the child questions, such as:

- How did you know that answer?
- Did you use a certain strategy to solve that problem?
- Which strategy did you use?
- How did you know to use that strategy?

Having this conversation during the assessment will give you a lot more information about where the student is with her automaticity than an old-fashioned timed test. If the child is stuck, this is the perfect opportunity for you to jump in with reminders of strategies that can nudge her in the right direction. It is a great time to even refer students back to their multiplication journal and make connections between the patterns they discovered during earlier instruction. Again, our job as teachers is to educate our students and help them make progress toward their goals. If all we're doing is assessing without constructive feedback, how is the child expected to make the most growth possible?

Helpful Hint! *Keep in mind that some students may never let you know that they're ready to assess, so you may want to have a system for calling on students on a regular basis.*

Celebrate

If the student is fluent in a particular set of facts, those cards are moved to the Celebrate part of the folder. Students then color in these newly memorized facts on their multiplication chart (found on the front of their folder). Some teachers choose to use a different color for each set of facts learned and include a key to show the date on which those facts were obtained. For example, if Taylor demonstrated fluency with her 6s, she would color in all of her 6 facts on her multiplication chart in pink. A pink line would be placed beside the multiplication chart with the date 2/5 to indicate that on February 5th, she showed that she knew her 6 facts.

Helpful Hint! *Create a classroom space, such as a basket, for students to place their folder when they are ready to be assessed. Then, as the day progresses and the time presents itself, the teacher or a classroom volunteer can take the folders and the students who are ready and quickly check to see how the students are progressing with their facts. This allows for small chunks of time to be maximized and for students' needs to be addressed on an individual basis. Some students may need to be more encouraged than others to contribute to the basket.*

Have Some Extra Time? Practice!

To provide students with something to always be working with, give students a game to add to their Practice folder pocket. The half-sheet games at the back of this book are the perfect size for students to put into their folders. It's nice to make practice part of their mathematical classroom routine. Working on their folders can be a warm-up once a week, a before-recess activity (you know, that weirdly empty five minutes that sometimes appears right before recess), or during a fluency station as part of your math workshop rotations.

Consider keeping the folders at a fluency station in your classroom or have students keep their folders on their desk for easy access. If students are ever "just waiting" for whatever reason, they can develop the habit of using that time to work on their goals. You will soon see that the opportunities for practice are endless!

When providing students with games that are not already printed on half-sized sheets of paper, consider two options:

- Print two copies of the game's directions on full sheets of paper so you can cut the paper in half and get two games from every one page of copying. They will fit nicely in the Practice side of the students' folders.
- Have students write or draw the directions to the games. That way they are doing the work and can practice sequencing directions in chronological order. (For detailed information, see page 118.)

Games and Activities

to Build Fluency in Multiplication and Division

CPA: (P, A)

Fast Factors

Objective: *Practice difficult multiplication facts*

Goal: *Get through the deck of cards as quickly and accurately as possible*

Group Size: *Partners, individual*

Materials: *a deck of cards with all face cards removed (Ace = 1)*

Students usually end up with a few factors that give them cause to pause. They often are the factors of 6, 7, and 8 that need additional practice and fluency work. This activity is great to target those tough-to-commit-to-memory facts. A reduced facsimile for including in the Practice side of the fluency folders is available on page 145.

Switch It Up!

Here are some modifications you may wish to try:

- *If a student has several facts that need practicing, she can create a pile of those factors, for example, one each of 6, 7, and 8. She then turns up one factor practice card and one card from the larger deck. This provides more purposeful practice of the facts in need of fluency.*
- *To scaffold this process a little, have students only work on the facts they know initially to build confidence. For example, if a student is working on his 6 factor as his practice factor, have him only use 2, 5, and 10 initially in his larger deck. This success will breed more success, and eventually additional factors can be added to the larger deck. The next factors could include 3 and 6. Remember, success breeds success, both for us learning how to teach without requiring timed tests, and for our students who are being asked to show deeper learning.*

Fast Factors

Goal: *Get through the deck of cards as quickly and accurately as possible*

Group Size: *Partners, individual*

Materials: *a deck of cards with all face cards removed (Ace = 1)*

Directions:

1. Decide what factor(s) you want to work on. Pull one of those cards from the deck. For example, if you are working on your facts that contain a factor of 7, pull a 7 from the deck.
2. Shuffle the remaining cards and place them face down.
3. Turn over a card from the deck and say the math fact using that card and your previously pulled card. For example, if you pulled a 7 and then turned over a 6, the fact you'd say is 7 x 6 = 42. Use a friend, a multiplication chart, or a calculator to check your work.
4. If you are correct, place your card to the side. If incorrect, the card goes to the bottom of the deck to be practiced again as it comes up in the pile.
5. Repeat Steps 3 and 4 until the deck is gone!

Game

CPA: (C, A)

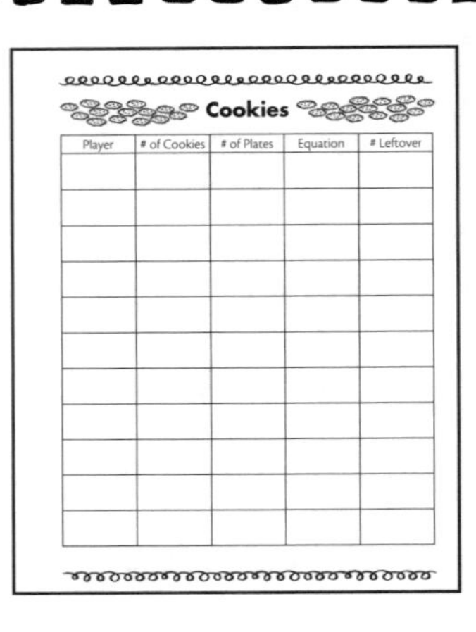

Cookies

Player	# of Cookies	# of Plates	Equation	# Leftover

Dividing Cookies

Objective: *Divide concretely using remainders and develop fluency with division facts*

Goal: *Collect the most cookies*

Group Size: *Small group*

Materials: *one die, 15 counters (to represent the "cookies"), six paper plates, recording sheet (see page 148 in the Reproducibles section)*

Students have a difficult time understanding how to work with remainders. This game provides a fun opportunity for students to practice equal-sharing as well as understanding what the remainder represents. In this game, students are actually going to want to have a remainder. What better way to learn this concept than by eating cookies? A reduced facsimile for including in the Practice side of the fluency folders is available on page 145.

Note: To add a new level of fun to this game, consider replacing the counters with pieces of a cookie cereal available in most grocery stores. Remember, however, to consider students' possible allergies before using food in the classroom.

As a literature connection, use the story ***The Doorbell Rang*** by Pat Hutchins.

DIFFERENTIATION

Switch It Up!

Here are some modifications you may wish to try:

- *Have stronger students use a larger start number.*
- *To support students who need it, allow students to use their multiplication and division chart to check their work throughout the game.*
- *Require recording of equations if students are ready for the abstract.*

Dividing Cookies

Goal: *Collect the most cookies*

Group Size: *Small group*

Materials: *one die, 15 counters (to represent the "cookies"), six paper plates, recording sheet*

Directions:

1. Set out the 15 counters or "cookies."
2. Player 1 rolls the die and takes the number of plates rolled.
3. Player 1 then divides the "cookies" (the whole) onto the plates (part). Player 1 keeps any cookies that could not divide equally. These are the remaining cookies (the remainder).
4. Slide the cookies from the plates and put them back into the middle of the table. Restack the plates.
5. Player 2 rolls and repeats Steps 2 through 4.
6. After playing several rounds, begin recording the equations on the recording sheet to show what happened during each turn.
   For example:
   15 cookies (whole) divided by 6 plates (part) equals 2 cookies per plate (part) with 3 cookies left over (a remainder of 3). Or 15 ÷ 6 = 2 r3 or 15/6 = 2 r3.
7. Play continues until all cookies have been kept (or "eaten").
8. The player who kept the most cookies wins.

CPA: (A)

Maze Multiplication

Objective: *Develop fluency with multiplication facts*

Goal: *Be the first player to get through the maze*

Group Size: *Small group*

Materials: *one or two decks of cards with all face cards removed (Ace = 1); game pieces such as chips, beans, buttons, etc. (one for each player); one die (this can be a standard die with factors 1–6, a modified die with one factor needing practice, or a modified die with factors greater than 6)*

Kids love mazes! This game is one that students will choose to play over and over again! It is a great way to practice facts that are giving them trouble, as well as reinforce those that have already been committed to memory. Note that to really solidify learning, you may wish to have students record their moves. A reduced facsimile for including in the Practice side of the fluency folders is available on page 146.

Note: When allowing students to play with two decks, make sure each is playing with a different colored or patterned deck to make sorting after the game is done easier.

Since you don't need a full deck, this game makes a great way to use leftover or lost cards. Students can grab any cards from your lost-card tub and line out their maze. This also makes it easier for you to grab out cards (such as 6, 7, and 8) that match students' specific needs.

DIFFERENTIATION

Switch It Up!

Here are some modifications you may wish to try:

- *Consider modifying the die to be specific to students' needs (i.e., if a student is working on his 5s, you can ensure the die being used includes 5s, or if a student is working on 7s and 8s, you could modify the die to include only 7s and 8s).*
- *For an extra challenge, use face cards. Jacks would equal 11, Queens 12, and Kings 13.*
- *Consider combining two decks of cards to make the maze longer.*
- *Instead of multiplying, this game can also be used to practice addition facts.*

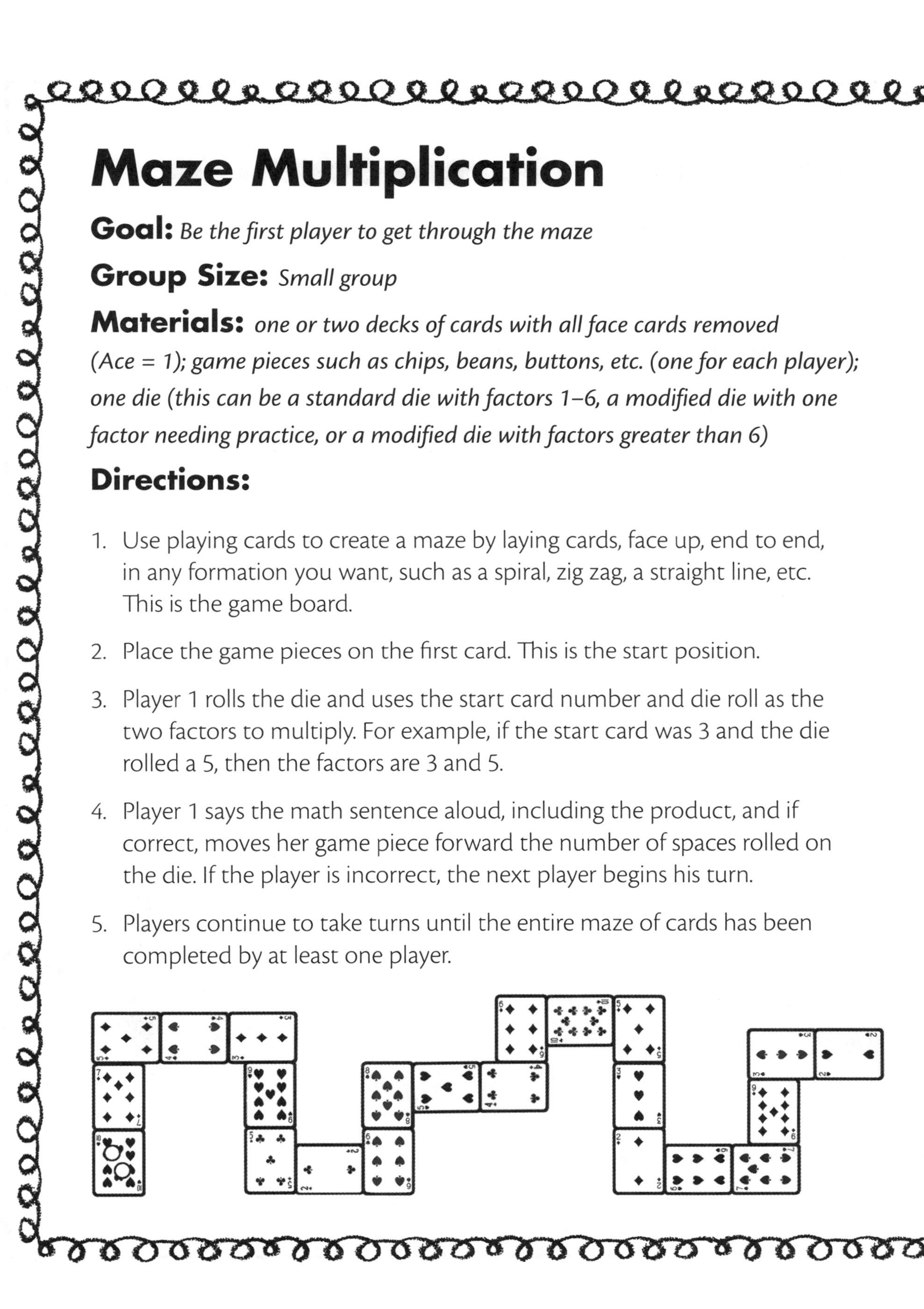

Maze Multiplication

Goal: *Be the first player to get through the maze*

Group Size: *Small group*

Materials: *one or two decks of cards with all face cards removed (Ace = 1); game pieces such as chips, beans, buttons, etc. (one for each player); one die (this can be a standard die with factors 1–6, a modified die with one factor needing practice, or a modified die with factors greater than 6)*

Directions:

1. Use playing cards to create a maze by laying cards, face up, end to end, in any formation you want, such as a spiral, zig zag, a straight line, etc. This is the game board.
2. Place the game pieces on the first card. This is the start position.
3. Player 1 rolls the die and uses the start card number and die roll as the two factors to multiply. For example, if the start card was 3 and the die rolled a 5, then the factors are 3 and 5.
4. Player 1 says the math sentence aloud, including the product, and if correct, moves her game piece forward the number of spaces rolled on the die. If the player is incorrect, the next player begins his turn.
5. Players continue to take turns until the entire maze of cards has been completed by at least one player.

Facts on the Forehead

Objective: *Develop fluency with multiplication facts*

Goal: *Collect the most cards*

Group Size: *Groups of three*

Materials: *a deck of cards with all face cards removed (Ace = 1)*

Facts on the Forehead provides a fun, almost silly, way for students to practice facts in an energetic and engaging format. This game can be played using the directions for partners as soon as facts are introduced. For a more challenging version of the game, have students play with the original directions. This game also allows for students to see the relationship between multiplication and division facts. A reduced facsimile for including in the Practice side of the fluency folders is available on page 146.

Note: With this game, modeling is very important. Consider inviting some of your most challenging students up to model the game with them. This will serve two purposes: Your most difficult students will have a heads-up on the game and may be less disruptive as you send them out to play, and this gives some of your most challenging students the attention they crave. However, this kind of attention is positive and related to math, so everyone benefits!

Because it is imperative that the product caller calls out the correct product, allow that student to use his multiplication chart to look up the correct product before calling it out if needed.

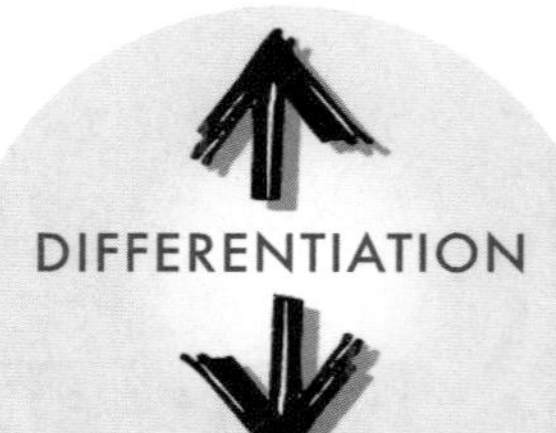

Switch It Up!

Here are some modifications you may wish to try:

- *Change the cards to match your students' level of understanding of the factors they are working on.*
- *Use this game with addition and subtraction facts.*

Facts on the Forehead

Goal: *Collect the most cards*

Group Size: *Groups of three*

Materials: *a deck of cards with all face cards removed (Ace = 1)*

Directions:

1. Choose the Product Maker.
2. Divide the deck of cards into two piles; each player who is not the Product Maker gets half of the cards.
3. The Product Maker counts down from 3.
4. At 0, the two players with cards hold their top card (or factor) face out on their forehead. **Note:** Each player cannot see his or her own card. Players can only see the other player's card.
5. The Product Maker says the product of the two factors.
6. Now that the product is known, the players holding cards must determine the factor on their forehead by using the known product and the other visible factor.
7. The first player to say his factor receives both cards.
8. Repeat steps until all factors have been played.

For an easier version, play with two players:

1. Choose a known factor. For example, if a player needs to work on her 5s, 5 will be the known factor for the entire game.
2. One player turns over a card and places it on her forehead.
3. The Product Maker (the other player) says the product.
4. The player holding the card finds her factor by using the known factor of 5 and the product provided.

CPA: (C, P, A)

10 x 10 Rekenrek

Objective: *Students use 10 x 10 rekenreks to demonstrate their understanding of multiplication factors and products*

Goal: *Show what you know!*

Group Size: *Whole class*

Materials: *10 x 10 rekenreks created from chenille stems (aka pipe cleaners), pony beads, and foam board or heavy mesh needlepoint canvas*

To create the 10 x 10 rekenrek, you can either extend any rekenrek style you've used in the past by using tagboard, needle point mesh, or foam board. Because it's larger, foam board is described here.

1. Cut a piece of foam board that will accommodate 10 rows of chenille stems spaced approximately an inch apart. Lay the foam board down as a portrait.
2. Poke 10 holes in a column on the left and 10 holes in a column on the right of the foam board. The holes need to be large enough to accommodate pushing the ends of the chenille stems through them.
3. Thread the beads on to the chenille stems.
4. As the 10 x 10 rekenreks are created—five of one bead color and five of another bead color per row—change the color order of the beads at 50 so students can see the difference between products less than or equal to 50 and those greater than 50 more easily. We recommend using the same two bead colors for the entire class to prevent students from focusing on color choices rather than math learning.
5. Secure the chenille stems on the board by folding down the chenille stems on the back and taping over these ends with duct tape.

To make life easier, be sure to prepare the foam board and the spaced holes in the board prior to students completing this activity.

Depending on students' level of independence, you may want to have a parent volunteer or support person make these ahead of time. Or, you can create a math center where students will create these to avoid waiting on students, in a whole-class setting, to finish. (Thanks to our friend and colleague Ricky for figuring this out for us.)

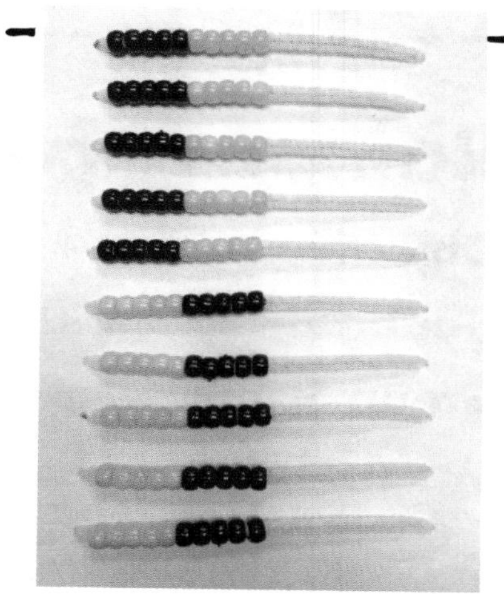

Photo credit goes to our colleague, Terri.

Note: We've included a reproducible for How to Make a Rekenrek for Less than $1.00 on page 144.

This activity uses the rekenrek to provide support for students on their way to understanding the concept of "groups of." This activity also helps students see the connection between the factors and their products because the beads can be arranged to see the products less than or equal to 50, as well as those greater than 50. Sample questions to ask after boards are created:

- *How can you show me the product of 15?*
- *Can you show it with 3 as one of the factors?*

Divisibility questions can also be asked.

- *How many groups of 7 can you make with 56 beads?*
- *Is 38 divisible by 2?*

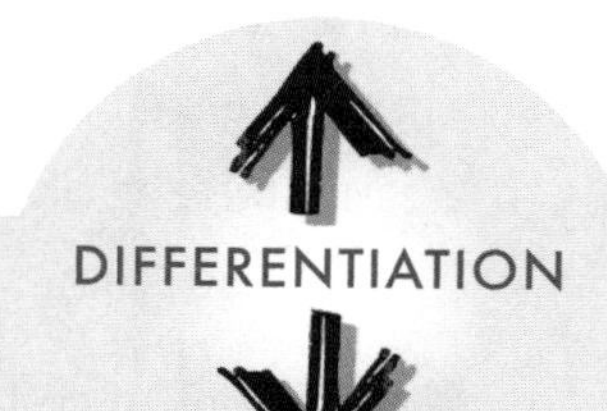

Switch It Up!

Here are some modifications you may wish to try:

- *Build these in conjunction with the multiplication journals so students see the multiplication facts both as arrays and as part of a 10 x 10 group.*
- *Have students use the 10 x 10 rekenreks to solve math stories of interest. Consider using content from other subject areas such as science, social studies, art, etc.*
- *There are apps available for most mobile devices (such as Number Racks) that can create various levels of rekenreks (from a 1 x 10 to a 5 x 10 and even above a 10 x 10) that can be used as a digital version for students if you don't want to physically make them with beads and chenille stems.*

CPA: (P, A)

Rainbow Factors

Objective: *To better understand factor pairs*

Goal: *Record all 100 numbers' factor pairs (over a period of time)*

Group Size: *Individual*

Materials: *paper and colored markers or pencils*

For ages, students have arranged factors in order when looking for greatest common factors. However, Rainbow Factors show students why they should do this and then gives them a visual to hook their thinking on while practicing their math facts and setting themselves up for future vocabulary and math work.

As students create their list of a number's factors, the arches (their rainbows), encourage them to begin with 1 and the number itself and then move through the other factors in order asking themselves, "Is there anything that multiplies by 2 that equals my number? Anything that multiplies by 3?" and so on.

As time goes on, you, as the teacher, can add in the additional vocabulary, such as "prime" and "square." Students can easily see that if a number's factors are only 1 and the number itself, it's a prime number because that's the definition of prime. Visually, they can see the lack of other factors. They can also see where square numbers are because they can make a 6 x 6, or a square-shaped, area model, to show the 6 x 6 factors. While some of this vocabulary is often taught in the higher grades, planting the ***prime***, ***composite***, and ***square*** seeds now will help their math minds grow and prep them to more easily understand the content later on.

A wonderful children's literature support piece is ***Two Ways to Count to Ten: A Liberian Folktale*** as retold by Ruby Dee.

Directions:

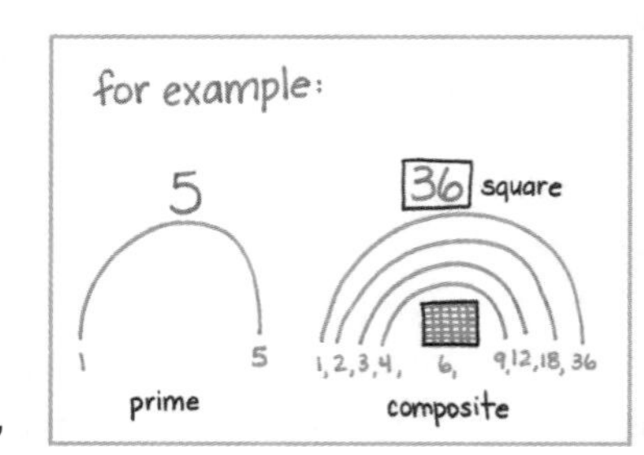

1. Have students create space on their papers for 100 numbers. This can be done on folded paper or in a student's journal. But don't worry: You won't be doing all 100 at once!
2. Model how to create an example of Rainbow Factors for several numbers, beginning with something simple such as 6. Say, "I know 1 and 6 are factors of 6, so I'll record them here."

- Write the 1 at the far left and the 6 at the right end of the "rainbow."
- Connect the two by drawing a large arc—this will be the outermost arc of the rainbow.
- Then say, "I also know that 2 and 3 are factors of 6. I will write these down, too." Record the 2 just after the 1, and the 3 just after the 2. Note to the students that you've listed the factors in numerical order.
- Draw a smaller arc connecting 2 and 3. Explain that the more factors a number has, the more arcs the finished rainbow will have.
- Repeat with another number, such as 12, to ensure students understand. This time, ask for volunteers to help you.

3. Remind students that these factors are the same as the arrays they built with manipulatives and the same as the area models they created earlier in their multiplication journals. Explain that Rainbow Factors are just a different pictorial representation.
4. Over a reasonable length of time, have students create their Rainbow Factors for the numbers 1–100.
5. Ask students: ***What do you observe as you create Rainbow Factors? How do these representations compare to your multiplication journal work with area models on graph paper?*** Have students write to respond to these questions and explain the connections and patterns they see.
6. Allow students to use this tool when working with multiplication or when working with equivalent fractions.

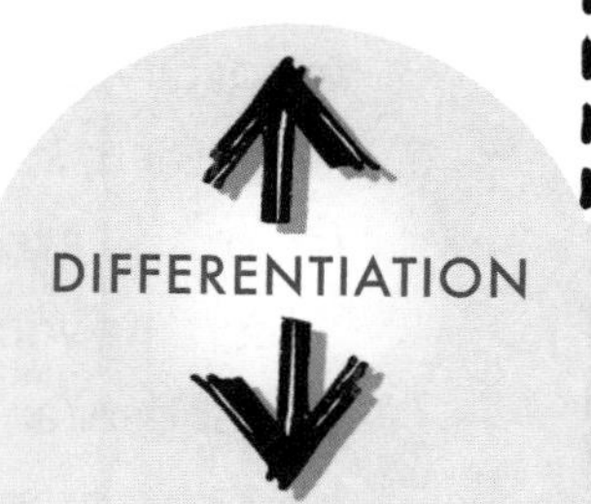

Switch It Up!

Here are some modifications you may wish to try:

- *Depending on students' readiness, you can incorporate other number sense vocabulary such as: prime, composite, square, least common multiple, greatest common factor, the divisibility rules, etc.*
- *You can make this activity a whole-class activity by dividing up the various numbers (smaller numbers for struggling students, larger numbers for more proficient students) and make a Rainbow Factor book for students to use as a resource tool.*

CPA: (P, A)

Multiple Multiples

Objective: *Create multiple creations using the list of multiples or the number itself as the graphic organizer*

Goal: *Create a multiple reference tool for finding the least common multiple (LCM)*

Group Size: *Individual*

Materials: *paper and colored markers or pencils*

Hint: *If a die-cut machine is available, create the large letter M and the numbers for students. They can then write directly onto the letter or number to create either or both of the activities listed. The letter M stands for multiple and is a graphic representation to help students find the least common multiple. Students list the multiples down each side of the M for the two numbers they're using. In the picture, we've listed the multiples of 4 down the left side and the multiples of 8 down the right side. Once we found the first common multiple, or the least common multiple (which happens to be 8 in this example), we recorded that in the center. It's the first multiple they have in common. It's like a Venn M (a Venn Diagram)!*

Students are expected to "count by" from an early age. These "count bys" are really their multiplication facts in order 2, 4, 6, 8, etc. Many students do not fully understand this connection, so this is a chance to solidify for them how knowing their "count bys" helps them know the multiplication facts for that factor and eventually will help them make sense of upcoming vocabulary. Students will need to transfer this understanding to the concept of multiples and least common multiples for support of fact fluency as well as future work with fractions. Multiple Multiples is one way to show students the connection in a nonstandard way.

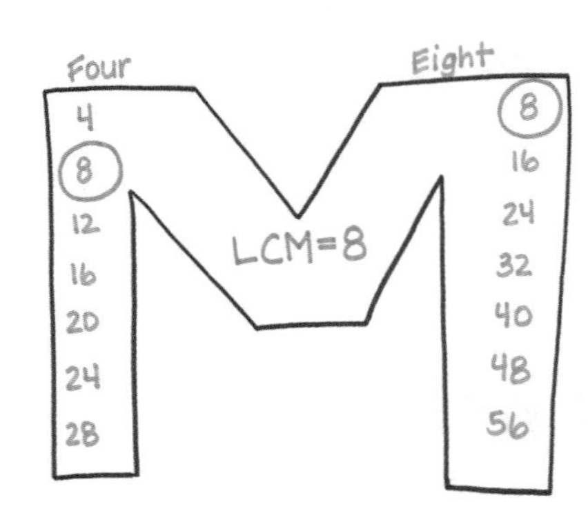

Directions:

1. Have students organize their factors for numbers 1 through 12. If doing this in a math journal, students can use one page for two numbers (one set of factors listed on the top half of the page, the other set on the bottom half of the page).
2. Have students record the "count bys" or multiples for numbers 1 through 12. For example, for the number 4, students would record 4, 8, 12, 16, 20, . . . and so on. This is also a great opportunity for students to show skip counting on a number line as a supporting representation of multiples.
3. Have students then record the multiples for each of their factors in this form.
4. To help create a connection to their previous work with their multiplication journals, ask students to look for patterns or connections between their 100s chart, their equation pages, and their newly created multiples.
5. As students progress with their understanding, have them go back in and look at what all multiples of 4 (or any other number) have in common to help them make sense of the divisibility rules. For example, students might point out that all of the multiples of 2, 4, and 8 are even numbers.
   Or, that when counting by (listing the multiples of) 5 and 10, the common multiples all end in a 0 because no whole number multiplied by 10 will give them a number ending in a 5.

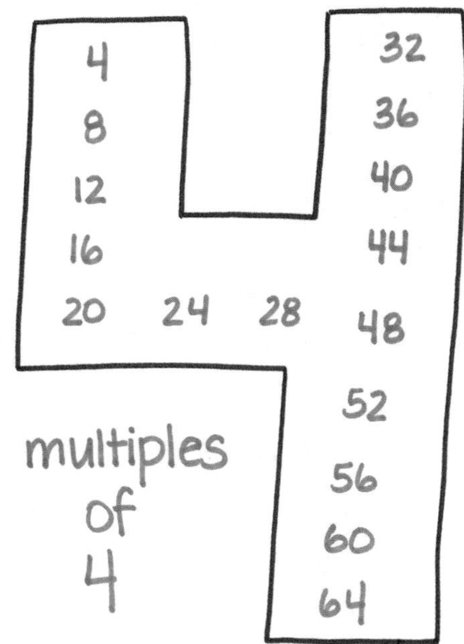

Note: If you do these multiples for these numbers on separate die-cut numbers or index cards, students can lay the multiples side-by-side and make the comparison that way.

CPA: (P, A)

Color Product Check

Objective: *Check partner's multiplication facts*

Goal: *Practice accuracy*

Group Size: *Partners, individual*

Materials: *multiplication chart (can also be used with an addition chart for a color sum check), acetate strips in two colors*

This tool can be used if students are struggling to line up the two factors for checking on a multiplication chart. It can also be used if two students are working together and one student may not be as automatic or proficient with correct answers as the other student.

You can place an addition or multiplication chart in a clear sheet for easy access and to protect it from multiple uses. Provide cut strips of acetate. Two different colors work well. As shown in the photograph, red and blue will end up showing the product in purple where they overlap. Students can keep their acetate strips in their clear sheets so they don't lose them and can access them when they need them. Here's an example of how this tool might look in your classroom:

Times Tables

X	1	2	3	4	5	6	7	8	9	10	11	12
1	1	2	3	4	5	6	7	8	9	10	11	12
2	2	4	6	8	10	12	14	16	18	20	22	24
3	3	6	9	12	15	18	21	24	27	30	33	36
4	4	8	12	16	20	24	28	32	36	40	44	48
5	5	10	15	20	25	30	35	40	45	50	55	60
6	6	12	18	24	30	36	42	48	54	60	66	72
7	7	14	21	28	35	42	49	56	63	70	77	84
8	8	16	24	32	40	48	56	64	72	80	88	96
9	9	18	27	36	45	54	63	72	81	90	99	108
10	10	20	30	40	50	60	70	80	90	100	110	120
11	11	22	33	44	55	66	77	88	99	110	121	132
12	12	24	36	48	60	72	84	96	108	120	132	144

When might students need them?

Sometimes, it's nice to slow students down a little bit and focus them on accuracy on their way to developing quickness or speed. This tool can do that. You can place two students together and ask that each person use this tool to check the other as they play games. This also allows students of different abilities to play together because each can check the work of the other.

Students can also use this tool when working independently. They now have access to their own "answer key." We believe it's better to have students look for a correct answer 1,000 times than to guess and memorize one answer incorrectly. To undo that incorrect answer can take much longer.

CPA: (P, A)

Multiple Ways to Multiply Bulletin Board

Objective: *Represent multiplication facts in multiple ways*

Goal: *Provide multiple ways to represent math facts and create an interactive bulletin board for reference*

Group Size: *Whole class*

Materials: *bulletin board that is divided up into a large multiplication chart, index cards, art materials*

Hint: *This task makes a great class display and is also a great task that can be used as a "when you are finished" activity. Students can create their fact pictures as time permits, representing their understanding in a myriad of ways.*

This bulletin board helps students create mental images of the multiplication facts they have been working so hard to understand. Everyone will be involved in creating this fantastic display for all to learn from and enjoy. Consider hanging this in a centralized location in your building to show off your students' work.

Directions:

1. Find a bulletin board that can be used for a display.
2. Mark off the bulletin board to represent a 10 x 10 multiplication grid.
3. After having taught students the meaning of multiplication, have students represent the various products with pictures and representations to finish the multiplication board.

DIFFERENTIATION

Switch It Up!

Here are some modifications you may wish to try:

- *Consider asking students to work on facts that are appropriate to their level of understanding. For example, a student at the early stages of understanding may create the pictures for 10s facts, while a more advanced student may create pictures for the 7s.*
- *You may wish to use this activity to create an addition table.*

CPA: (C, P, A)

Array of Arrays

Objective: *Find arrays in everyday life*

Goal: *Contribute to the class Array of Arrays*

Group Size: *Whole class*

Materials: *images and items representative of arrays*

Hint: *If the storage of actual items becomes an issue, take photos of the items brought in for the Array of Arrays and use the photos in lieu of the actual items. Also, you may want to collect student-appropriate magazines from which students can cut pictures.*

Once students start to understand the concept of an array, it can be used to make a great visual display—an Array of Arrays—which will help them see that arrays of all kinds appear every day. They'll realize arrays will show up from today and for the rest of their lives as mathematicians. This activity will help students become more attentive to the world around them.

This activity can be done for other math concepts as well. Consider creating a bulletin board titled Math in Our World. As students find items, pictures, etc. of math vocabulary and concepts they have learned, they can add it to the bulletin board. Be sure to have students write a small statement describing the math that can be identified.

Switch It Up!

Here are some modifications you may wish to try:

- *As a challenge, have students create their own array book with an array representing the factors from 1 through 12.*
- *Create a class book of all the array pictures. This not only creates a reference for students, but a wonderful sense of class pride.*

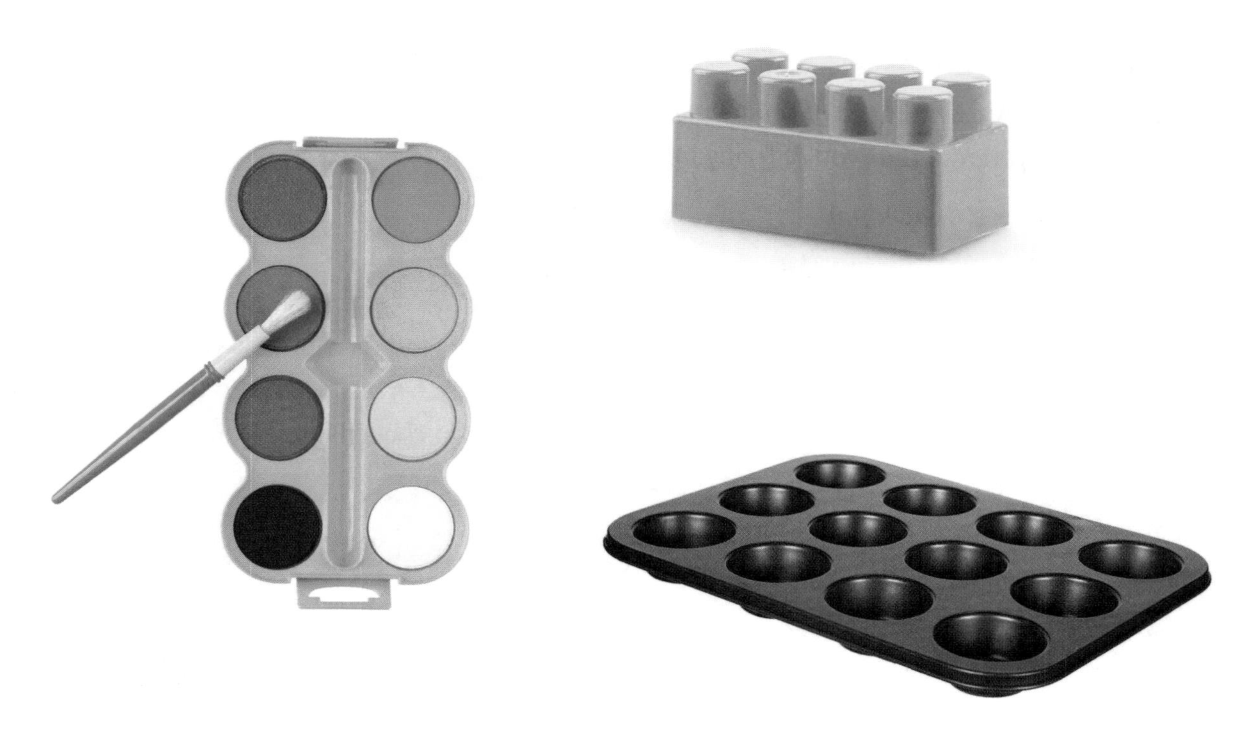

Directions:

1. Have students collect actual items, images of items, or drawn pictures of items that represent arrays.
2. Have students label their contributions and add them to the class display of arrays, or have them add it to their individual book collection of arrays after sharing it with the class. As students work on this activity, some questions you could ask to deepen understanding are:
   - What product is most often represented as an array in our array collection?
   - Do most of our arrays show even products or odd? Why?
   - What are some items organized as arrays in our real world?
3. Challenge the class to collect a representation for each of the arrays up through a 12 x 12.

CPA: (A)

Factor Find

Objective: *Find different factors that make up the chosen number*

Goal: *Use as many of the numbers in the 10 x 10 grid as possible to create the product that you're trying to find*

Group Size: *Individual*

Materials: *teacher-created grids for various products*

Students like puzzles, and teachers like differentiation. Factor Find is an activity that allows for both needs to be met. However, note that this activity takes a bit more prep than most, but it's well worth it because it provides a great and fun challenge for students. You need to pre-make each puzzle for students to work on. However, to make getting started with this activity easier, a reproducible of a 10 x 10 grid can be found on page 158. Directions to create these puzzles for students are provided on the next page.

Switch It Up!

Here are some modifications you may wish to try:

- *Although usually played alone, this game also permits pairs of students to work on the same puzzle and check each other's combinations. The person who wrote the most equations or has the fewest numbers left could be determined to be the "winner."*
- *Students can create puzzles for other students once they see how the puzzles work.*
- *Use smaller factors to force the use of the Associative Property. For example, if the product is 12, students could use (1 x 2) + (1 x 2) + (2 x 4) = 12. Or, they could do (2 x 3) x 2 = 12, or (2 x 4) + (6 - 2).*
- *For an extra challenge, have students graph the various combinations they find. For example, how many 7 x 8 combinations did they find? How many (2 x 4) x 7 combinations were there?*

Directions:

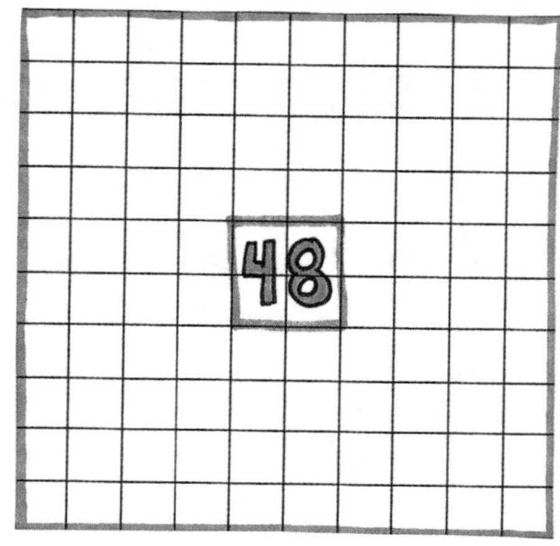

1. Using a 10 x 10 grid, a product is determined that has multiple factors and combinations of factors. This product is the large number recorded in the center of the grid. For example, if using the product of 48, it would be placed in the center. 48 is a good candidate because there are multiple factors that can be used, including 1, 2, 3, 4, 6, 8, 12, 16, and 48.
2. Fill in all of the remaining empty squares with numbers. These numbers should include a lot of factors for the number, but they can also include some nonfactor numbers to provide a challenge for students. For example, with the number 48, you could use some 5s and 7s. They aren't factors of 48, but they could provide a chance for students to create that number in a unique way. For example, 48 = (4 x 5) + (7 x 4).
3. The student tries to find as many combinations of factors for the given product as possible and records the number sentences below the grid. Factors or numbers used in a number sentence need to be adjacent.
4. Various properties can be used as well. In fact, this constant connection to properties should be encouraged. For example, if the product is 56, some possible combinations might be 7 x 8, (2 x 4) x 7. Students working at the basic level can work with just the traditional multiplication facts that will make up the product. Students who are seeking a challenge can push themselves to find less common equations.

6	2	4	3	3	2	4	3	5	6
12	6	3	6	2	6	3	4	8	2
1	3	2	2	3	2	9	4	6	2
12	3	2	6	1	12	6	2	3	4
1	2	1	2	12		3	4	2	2
7	3	12	2			4	3	2	4
7	2	9	3	3	4	2	2	3	3
1	2	12	1	4	3	3	1	12	6
2	12	2	6	1	12	4	12	1	2
1	2	6	3	4	4	3	2	2	3

1 x 12 = 12
4 x 3 = 12
(2x2) x 3 = 12

5. When no more combinations are available, the numbers that have been used can be added up to find the score (in this case, highest score would win) or the numbers not used can be added up to create a score (in this case, the lowest score would win).

CPA: (P, A)

Game Sketch-Noting

Objective: *Communicate how to play a game learned in class*

Goal: *Create a visually appealing and accurate set of directions for a learned game*

Group Size: *Whole class, individual*

Materials: *game template (if desired)*

The idea of never working harder than your students and not doing for your students what they can do for themselves can both be epitomized when students record the directions for games in their own way, often using visuals versus words. The clever thing about this activity is that so many skills—writing, art, communication—are used at once.

Switch It Up!

Here are some modifications you may wish to try:

- *Maintain a class chart of game icons. For example, two stick figures can represent two players, or a light bulb can represent the game's goal.*
- *Have a student or several students sketch-note the directions for all of the games. Then compile all of the games for the year, copy and bind them, and present the finished product as an end-of-the-year present for students to take home.*
- *Send home a sketch-noted game each month for parents or guardians to use with their children at home.*
- *Create a teacher Big Book on chart paper of all of the games as a resource.*

Directions:

1. Brainstorm a list of game words students will need.
2. Create a visual library of words that appear frequently.
3. Give students the basic criteria that should be contained in the sketch-noted directions.
4. Teach the game through the sketch-noting process, modeling not only how to play the game, but also ideas for capturing the essence of the game.
5. Allow students to play the game.
6. Provide time and supplies for students to revise, edit, and decorate their game directions.

PART 4: If Not Timed Tests... Then What?

PART 4: If Not Timed Tests... Then What?

Timed tests seem to be a time-honored tradition. But the more conversations we have about the topic, the more consistent, anxiety-filled stories we hear from both those who took timed tests and those who wonder what they can do instead of giving them. Not everything we've always done is worth doing over and over again. It is our belief that your time, and your students' time, can be better spent. We hope we've provided you with plenty of ideas to develop students' fluency from whole-class activities, to journals, to folders, to games. We encourage you to use concrete, pictorial, and abstract instructional practices to teach an understanding of the facts, which is so much more valuable than just rote memorization, and we hope you're starting to see what we so firmly believe—that there are viable alternatives to timed tests.

It Only Makes Sense

Let's do some basic math. Imagine you have 170 instructional days in the year. Note that we've subtracted 10 days from the typical 180-day school year to account for the beginning of school, testing days, field trips, and other events that come up that interrupt instructional days. In reality, there are probably even fewer instructional days in your school year, but we wanted to be optimistic.

Let's also imagine that each timed test—from handing out the tests, taking the tests, collecting the tests, grading the tests, and recording the scores—takes 7 minutes (which is a conservative guess as it doesn't account for the teacher prep time, but it's a safe average).

So, that's 170 days multiplied by 7 minutes. This equals 1,190 minutes. Divide this number by 60 and you now have 19.8 hours. For the sake of easier math, we'll round it to 20. Twenty hours is equal to over three school days (figuring each is a 6-hour day) of instructional time that is spent on giving or taking timed tests.

Even if you're not giving timed tests, we bet you're doing something that could be replaced with something else that would help your students develop proficiency with their math facts.

Your time and your students' time could and should be better spent. Now, with our help and the art of teaching you already had, you are armed with a lot of choices you can use in your instruction, and we hope you now see (and agree) that timed tests aren't a viable option. As we tell our young people, once we ***know*** better, we must ***do*** better.

The most common questions we hear at this point, after we've provided alternatives to the instruction piece many of us thought we were getting from doing timed tests day in and day out is this: ***How will I assess students if I don't give timed tests? What will I do instead to find out what my students know?***

One thing to keep in mind is that teaching should take up the majority of your time. We as teachers know this, but we also feel a lot of pressure to collect and record data on our students. Please know that you will still be able to gather a lot of important data doing the suggested activities we've provided. You'll be gathering evidence daily about your students and their work toward fact fluency and overall number sense. This formative assessment data will inform students' learning and will inform your teaching—sometimes in the very moment you see it.

More formal assessments should then only confirm what you already knew about your students' understanding. We must remember that testing, in and of itself, does not teach. Timed tests don't teach—they provide a score. But because assessment is a real part of our world, we would like to conclude our book by looking at (and answering) the question, "How will I assess students if I don't give timed tests?"

In the following pages, we hope to provide you with organizational ideas for recording what you're seeing and learning about your students both formally and informally. Read on to learn about a few quick alternative assessments.

Conferencing

Move around to students and have individual conversations. Ask questions to help you determine your students' levels of proficiency.

The power of questioning and demonstrating during these conferences cannot be overrated. Some questions you may want to ask during these conferences are:

- How do you know?
- Can you please show me the multiples of 4?
- Can you tell me about the pattern when multiplying by a 10?
- What are the factors of 36?
- How do you know 7 isn't a factor of 48?
- What are two ways to show 7 x 7 = 49?
- Could 63 be a product when multiplying a whole number by 4? Why or why not?

When asking a student to show you something, have him show you with manipulatives, with pictures, and/or with numbers on a whiteboard. This may feel less formal. If you'd like permanent documentation or evidence, take a quick photo of the student's work, or have the student record his understanding in his math journal.

Consider creating a chart and system for showing student growth. The chart could be very simple with just names, facts, and proficiency level. This is assessment, and it can replace a timed-test score. For example:

Student Name	x10 facts	x5 facts	x2 facts
Jason	PP P P	NY	
Taylor	P NY P	P P	
Maribeth	P	P P	

In this chart, the P represents Proficient, meaning there was evidence that understanding was present. PP represents Partially Proficient, or the understanding is developing and is partially there. If no evidence was seen, an NY can be written to indicate Not Yet. In this example, multiple conferences have taken place, so there are multiple pieces of evidence for each column.

Or you may prefer an even simpler recording method for conferencing, such as this:

Student Name	Doubles	Doubles+1	+10	+9
Mitchell	+	+	+	-
Brett	+	+	+	-
Camryn	-	+	+	+

The (+) indicates they've got it, and the (-) indicates that they don't have it quite yet. This information can be collected periodically to show growth over time or collected cumulatively to show overall work toward mastery of their facts. You can record this information on a daily basis, on an as-needed basis, on a watching-a-specific-game basis, or whenever it makes sense for you and your classroom structure.

The conference could also be more intensive and more directed. Imagine taking the time you used to spend administering timed tests and instead, using that time to spend with one or two students one-on-one to see where they are in their progress toward fluency. While you're conferencing, other students can be doing self-work toward fluency such as a quick individual game or activity or working on the previously described fluency folder.

As you conference, be thinking, ***What will my next instructional steps be to meet THIS student's needs?*** Do you see how this differs from just knowing that Eddie got 45 out of 100 for the 10th day in a row? Instead, now you may have noticed that Eddie doesn't quite know his 4 facts. You can specifically teach to that skill and make progress toward fluency by focusing on the skill needed, not just the speed.

Here are a few basic, yet helpful rules to follow while conferencing:

1. Ask good questions.
2. Be a listener.
3. Observe and record.
4. Plan next instructional steps.

Anecdotal Records

You can also record individual observations of students' achievements and struggles by recording hand-written notes indicating levels of fluency. This can be done during conferencing or during daily classroom instruction and activities, but these are qualitative notes taken specifically to target each child and their successes and their struggles. If needed, these qualitative observations could be compiled into a quantitative representation that can be just as valid as any numerical recording.

Structured Charts

This practice might look like:
Multiple students per page . . .

Student Name	Understands Groups of	Can show multiplication as an area model/array	Understands multiplication as repeated addition	Can show multiplication on a number line
Isabelle	11/12 played Group It successfully through 12s	2/5 multiplication journal done independently	3/15 explained multiplication as repeated addition to Olivia	No evidence as of 4/1
Mitchell	11/12 played Group It successfully overall, struggling with 7s		4/17 showed multiplication as repeated addition in math journal	

. . . or one student per page.

Isabelle Starting facts known: 0, 1, and 5	
Understands Groups of	11/12 played Group It successfully through 12s
Can show multiplication as an area model/array	2/5 multiplication journal done independently
Understands multiplication as repeated addition	3/15 explained multiplication as repeated addition to Olivia
Can show multiplication on a number line	No evidence as of 4/1

The most important thing to keep in mind about the chart you use is that the design of your record-keeping system needs to match your organizational structure as an educator.

You can make note of any evidence showing that the understanding is present or which error is being made that is inhibiting understanding. Some teachers prefer to have a document for each student, while others prefer to see more than one student on a page. The organization is up to you to plan and execute; the learning is up to the child to show. We as teachers just have to be there to see it, hear it, and record it.

Some teachers prefer a less structured method to gather information. We've collected a bunch of our favorite effective methods for recording anecdotal notes here. Don't be afraid to use a variety of methods. In time, you'll have your favorites that you use (and maybe even tweak!) year after year.

Sticky Notes

There are many ways to use the great teaching tool of a sticky note. One way is to put out student notes on a clipboard numbered to correspond to your student's class number. For example, if Hayden is number 1 on your class list, rather than write her name on every sticky note, you might write #1. As the week goes by, you gather evidence for all of the students in your class and record what you see on each student's sticky note. You can quickly see which students you haven't visited with, observed, or taken note of by seeing which sticky notes are still blank.

Some teachers have also created blank sheets of paper in a binder—one sheet per student. While walking around, working in guided math groups, etc., they write down the student's name, date, and a quick observation on a sticky note. Then, at the end of the day (or week), they transfer the sticky note to the student's corresponding data page.

Sticky Labels

A quicker, easier, but a little less cost effective way to monitor student progress is to type each student's name on a sticky label. There are usually about 30 per page, so a class will often fit on one label page. Each week, simply take the sheet for that week and gather information about students' work toward fluency. By the end of the week, each label should have been filled in and can be added to a notebook or filing system.

You can even add additional information to the label if looking for a specific skill across the entire class. For example, if you've just taught Doubles and Doubles + 1, you may have that information already pre-filled in on the labels. Then, all you have to do is add a letter (P for Proficient), or a symbol (+, for got it), or even a check mark to indicate that you saw it.

Class List and a Highlighter

This is one of the simplest methods and only takes a little bit of preparation. In a Word document, create small class lists. You can usually fit about four class lists per page. Cut the lists apart into small strips of paper. As you teach a specific skill—for example, counting on by 1—write the skill name at the top of the class list. When you see a student successfully counting on by 1, highlight her or his name. Or, for example, Factor 8 could be written at the top, and when students know their multiplication facts for 8, you could highlight the student's name. When all students are highlighted, celebrate! Until each name ***is*** highlighted, however, this list becomes a list of "who still needs to learn that specific skill." This list can also be provided to a support person in your classroom so she knows exactly who needs what skill as she pulls together her small groups.

Helpful Hint! *This list-and-highlighter method is also GREAT for keeping track of who has returned the permission slip for a field trip or other activity. Clip the list to the returned slips, highlight the names of those who've brought back their forms, and stay focused on those who still need to turn in theirs. This method also works well for homework, assignments, and a myriad of other classroom-related tasks and tools beyond marking fluency proficiency.*

Index Card Flip Folder

This is one idea for organizing student data that has been around a long time, but it can be extremely useful for keeping all of the students' information in one place.

Begin by labeling a file folder Addition/Subtraction Fluency or Multiplication/Division Fluency. Next, open the folder and tape an index card at the bottom. Record a student's name at the bottom of the card. Then, tape another index card (labeled with the next student) on top of the first, making sure you don't cover the first student's name; position the second card so the name at the bottom of the first card shows. Continue this process until the file folder is full on both sides and each student in your class has an index card. Now, as you see demonstrations of proficiency, you can quickly open the folder, flip to the index card for that particular student, and record whatever form of evidence you need.

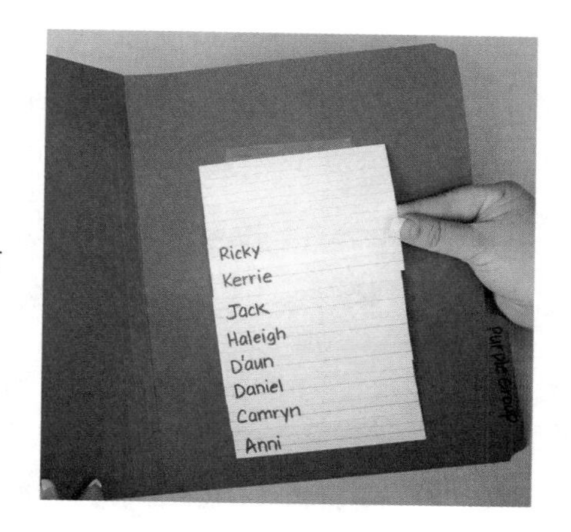

Specific Alternative Assessment Ideas

Hiding Counters Assessment

Primary teachers need to determine each student's number to focus on based on what they know about student understanding at the time of assessing. To do this, ask a student to count out 5 counters. Pay close attention to how he gives you the 5 counters. Did he use 1-to-1 counting? Did they pull a group of 2 and then a group of 3? Did he orally count to 5, but only have 4 counters? These observations will allow you to see if the student is ready to move beyond 1-to-1 correspondence and start looking at combinations.

Once you have the 5 counters, tell the student that you are going to hide some behind your back, and he will need to identify how many are missing. Put 3 counters in your hand behind your back, and open your other hand to reveal 2 counters. Pay attention to how the child figures out the answer. What you are looking for is automaticity—can the child, within a reasonable amount of time, identify the missing number of 3? If the student is successful, show him a different number. Ask the child to tell you what strategy he is using to determine the missing number. These are great notes to record on an anecdotal recording chart.

Once you determine the child has combinations to 5, check for understanding of combinations for 10. Combinations of 5 and 10 are the easiest combinations for students to see. If they are successful with 10, then go back and check for combinations of 6, then 7, then 8, and then 9.

However, if a student struggled with combinations to 5, back down to 4. And if 4 was difficult, go ahead and check combinations for 3; perhaps this student needs to go back to counting and cardinality activities.

Once you have determined a child's target number, provide him or her with opportunities to practice making combinations with that number. Check in with students about every other week and record their progress on one of the above suggested organization techniques or on a tool of your own.

Journal Responses

For journal responses, you could begin by posing questions to students that would elicit their knowledge about facts and their connections. For example, you could ask: ***How does knowing 2 x 8 help you understand 4 x 8?*** or ***How can you use 8 + 5 to figure out 8 + 6?*** Students' responses to these questions will give you a clear idea of connections students are making between facts.

When students are beginning to learn the variety of addition strategies and have been able to attach language to these strategies, having them process this thinking in their journals can be a powerful way to gain insight into their understanding and help them permanently cement their understanding in their own words.

Students are capable of amazing things when asked the right question and given the opportunity to explain their thinking. Here is a wonderful example to demonstrate:

In this picture, one of our students was asked to show 8 + 6 + 2 and then explain his thinking. As you can see, this student clearly understands the idea of making 10 to solve a problem. We also learn a lot from this student's truck that drives the two pieces up to complete the 10-frame that already contained 8. When the "full house" is combined with the 6 in the adjacent house, the total is 16.

Doesn't this picture speak louder and tell us more than a timed test would have when checking to see if a student understands making 10? Now, we understand that this isn't the most efficient strategy because of the time taken to draw the response (including the cute truck carrying up the two counters). As a teacher, we'd want to now ask and collect answers to these or similar questions:

- What does this child know?
- What else could I ask to see what else the child knows?
- What would my next instructional steps be with this child?
- What prompting feedback could I provide to find out more?
- Do I need another piece of evidence to know the child understands making 10 as a strategy?

In another journal entry, a student showed the various bonds to make 6. As you can see in this journal page, the student clearly shows 0 + 6 = 6 and 6 + 0 = 6. While this page may have been drawn during instruction, we can use it for assessment, too. The student is able to represent what she knows with pictures, number bonds, and words, and she then even expresses an understanding that the reason she can do this is because of a property. She explains it as, "I did thuy koonim te poprdt." (Translation: "I did the Commutative Property.")

To ensure this student has a firm grasp on this information, we could ask her to do another similar problem and see if we get the same response. We could ask her to tell us more about the "koonim te poprdt" (Commutative Property). Such as: ***Why is it called that? Does the Commutative Property work for subtraction, too?*** As students draw or write responses in their journals, our job is to see them for what they are and to try and find out more. We then use all of that information to confidently say, "Yes, this child has it," or, "This child doesn't have it yet; what do we both (student and teacher) need to do next?"

Helpful Hint! *To remember what prompt you gave your students, type up the prompts in a slide show program and use a large font. When printed out, each question will then appear in a small square that students can cut apart and tape into their journals for future reference. The slide show program is also nice because you can post it on an interactive whiteboard, students can have their own copy, and you can modify it year to year to match your students' needs.*

Open Timing

Provide students with a set of problems and give them as much time as they need to complete the chosen set of facts. Time is recorded, but it is not a race against a clock; rather, the time is used as a check-in opportunity. Make a note of students' strategies, progress, etc. This kind of alternate assessment is only done a few times a year. The goal is to show improvement, not meet a specific speed goal against the other students.

We encourage you to allow students to have their multiplication chart out to use while taking the test. They can record answers they have to look up with a pen, while products they know mentally are recorded in pencil. It will take them time to look up the answer; however, the goal here is understanding. The speed will come once the understanding is developed. When using this approach, note how often they use the chart. The goal is for them to access it less and less. Remember that every time a child writes an incorrect answer, that is a way of thinking that you have to undo. As we mentioned earlier, we would rather a child look up a fact's answer 1,000 times and get it right than write it incorrectly even once.

Pattern Proof

Provide a page to encourage students to use patterns such as Doubles or Doubles + 1. Ask students to solve the problems AND explain the patterns that help them solve. You can learn as much from what they ***don't*** use as from what they ***do*** use.

Another way to get students to look at patterns is something we learned from our colleague and friend, Jane Felling. Give students a regular page of facts. The twist is they are going to look through this full page of math problems and categorize them by strategy.

For example, if they can use doubles, they might circle in red all of the facts solvable with the doubles strategy. Not only does this show you if they understand the strategy, it also shows the student how much they ***do*** know when they look at a page full of facts.

Teach your students the terminology of the "known fact." This is and should be an acceptable strategy and one that we should be allowing students to use to explain their thinking. However, we also want to encourage students to think about what they'd do if they couldn't remember the known fact. We want them to have a Plan B. Students should always know to ask themselves, "What thinking or strategy would I rely on if I don't have a known fact? Is there another way to solve this problem?"

Game Observations

Provide a game for students to play. While students are playing the game, all you need to do is act as an observer and a questioner. Basically, you are looking for the three components of fluency—understanding, efficiency, and accuracy. The most difficult part of using this alternative assessment is setting up the students to play a game with the skills you need to see and document. The benefit of this approach, however, is that you can observe and record data on several students at once.

You don't always need to be just the observer. If you have students record their work, you can also look at their recorded version later. This way you have student-generated written records, as well as your first-hand observations. You'll know whether they did the work alone, or with support. You'll know if they used tools and resources to find the answer, or did it without. You'll be able to see their level of confidence while completing the game.

List of Facts

When students are learning how to read, they are often assessed on their sight words. They are presented with a short list or small pile of words, and it becomes clear which words they know and which they do not. With this in mind, we got to thinking . . . why don't we do this with math facts, too? First, you gather the facts you've been teaching. For example, if you've been working on multiplying by 6, you could have a list of math facts including the factor 6, or a stack of flashcards including the factor 6. Then, you show students the facts. Students then solve what they can, pass when they're not ready, or move on to the next fact when too much time has passed. The key to this is working in small chunks, a safe environment, and individualized sessions so that students can move at their own pace and still receive a lot of specific feedback. You gain individual assessment data and have next steps (the ones they didn't know, or the next fact in the sequence) to guide them and you. This could be done as a pre-assessment, a benchmark check-in during instruction, or a post assessment.

Helpful Hint! *Consider creating and assessing these lists in the order of instruction, leading to mixed facts. For example, if you began with one of the factors as 10, assess this. Then, move on to 5s, and then possibly assess 10s and 5s. Eventually, you'll be able to mix the facts and get a true feel for a student's proficiency.*

Student Response Cards

Provide students with some sort of response device; this could range from digit cards to some sort of digital response system, such as a clicker system. There are even free apps available for this purpose. As you ask a fact question, the student holds up the answer, allowing for individual accountability. You can move as quickly as desired, while monitoring who is keeping pace and who isn't. By modifying the amount of response time, you give all students an entry point, and you can control the volume of problems as well as the purpose.

Recall

The whole point of fluency with math facts is so that students are more fluid when it comes to solving larger operation computation, solving math stories, or doing more complex problem-solving. One way to assess a student's proficiency with fluency is to take note of their recall during problem-solving events. This gives you feedback about their fluency as well as their comprehension of the math facts.

We said early on that math facts are to math what sight words are to reading. If that's the case, then these math facts help us "read" and comprehend the math we're being asked to do. When not being required to "sound out" each fact, we can make sense of the task and what the learner is supposed to demonstrate.

In Conclusion

While this book of ideas and alternatives is not exhaustive, you've probably been reminded of or developed some of your own unique approaches now that you've read ours. Keep thinking, keep adding new games, activities, and methods; let the end of this book be just the beginning for you.

Writing this book and helping others make the decision to leave timed tests behind has become a personal mission for us, a passion we share often, wherever and whenever we can.

We're still on our journey. We're still learning, still fine tuning and tweaking our work with students, and we know you are, too.

But, throughout this book we hope we've

- made our case for why giving up the long-held tradition of using timed tests as the main method of instructing and/or assessing math facts is necessary, and
- helped you see the need to put the development of understanding first and foremost when thinking about fluency.

Our students only get one go-around at their early education. They have this small window of time that sets them up for those later years, when there will be larger, more serious consequences for those who have not developed a solid foundation in math facts. How they see themselves as mathematicians during this time will influence decisions they make today and for the rest of their lives. We don't want them to shut down on math because of their experiences with timed tests.

Instead, we hope they engage with the learning process, with the material. We hope they seek challenges. We hope they persevere. We hope they feel success and learn from failure. This is our hope for our students, your students, and for you. We believe this can be accomplished with your good instruction and their good attitudes.

Our students are ready for the change. The bigger and more important question is: Are ***you*** ready for the change now that you've learned about how different teaching and learning could look? Just image it—there could be an entire generation of students who don't have a timed test story to tell.

Time's up on timed tests . . . let's do this!

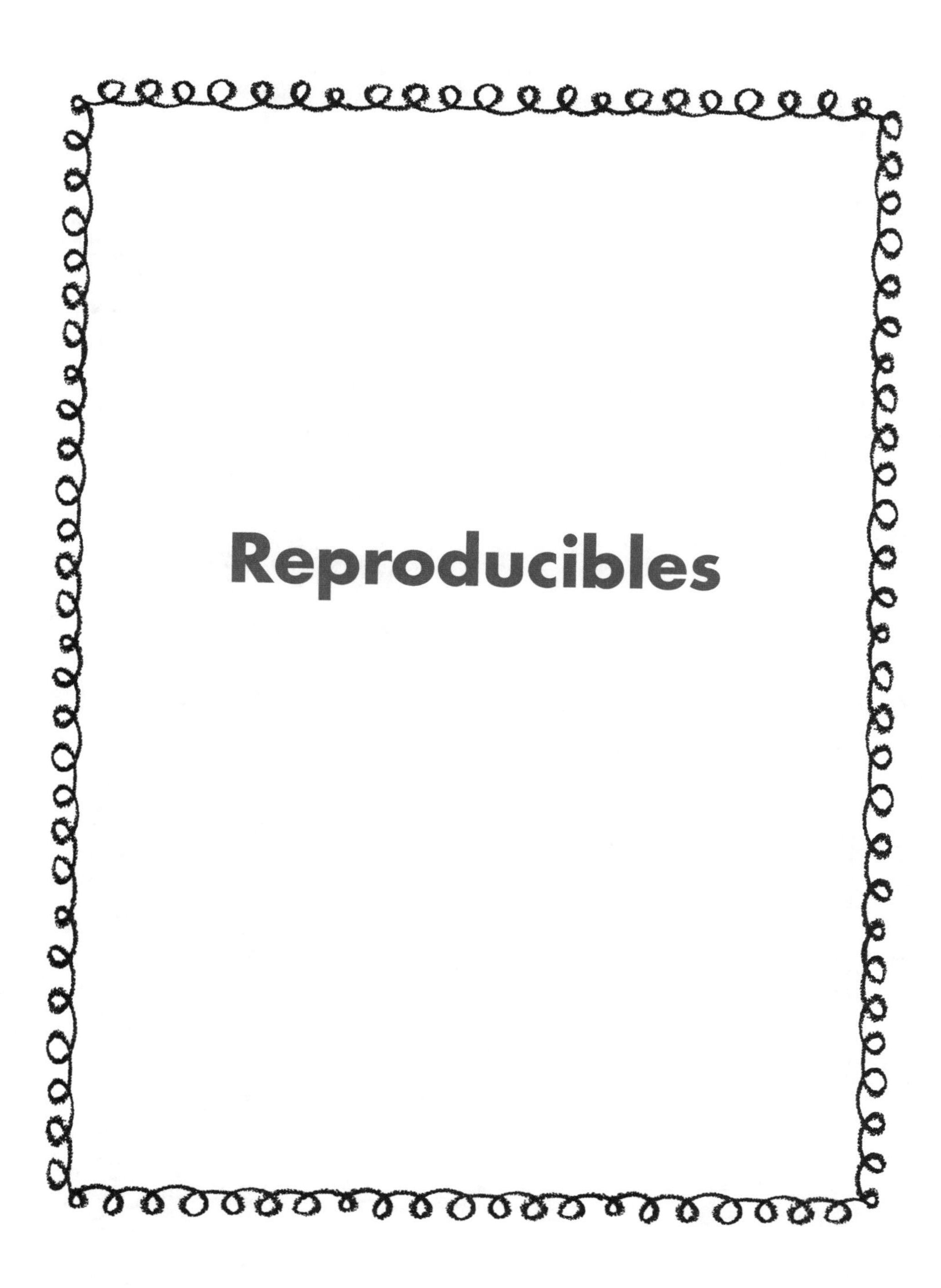

Reproducibles

Timely 10s

Goal: *Make a 10*

Group Size: *Individual*

Materials: *double 10-frame board, two-color counters or two different colors of another manipulative, Timely 10s recording sheet, two 10-sided dice*

Directions:

1. Roll the dice.
2. Use the two-color counters on the double 10-frame to represent the two numbers rolled. Be sure to complete the first 10-frame before filling in the second 10-frame. For example: If you roll an 8 and a 5, show 8 red counters and 5 yellow counters.
3. On the Timely 10s recording sheet, record the original equation and the equation for the way it looks on the 10-frame. For example: $8 + 2 = 10$, and $10 + 3 = 13$.
4. Continue rolling the dice, representing the numbers with counters on the double 10-frame and recording the equations.

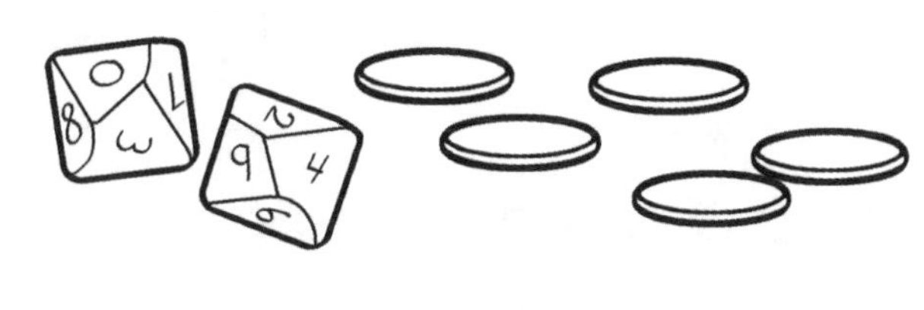

Sum-thing Special

Goal: *Be the player with the highest total sum of cards at the end of the game*

Group Size: *Partners*

Materials: *two decks of cards with all face cards removed* (Ace = 1)

Directions:

1. Both players turn over two cards each at the same time. The cards should be placed side by side in front of the player—one card to the left side, and one card to the right side. Once the cards are placed, the order cannot be switched around. Each player adds her own cards together and says the sum.
2. The player who has the higher sum takes both cards that are in the right-side position (each player's right-side pile) and puts them off to the side into a special pile. Each player needs to keep her own special pile because it will be used later.
3. Players then put the card left on the table (the card that was on the left side) at the bottom of their draw pile.
4. Play continues until players are out of cards in their draw pile.
5. Now players collect all the cards from their special pile and add them together. The player with the greater sum wins.

Bowling for 10

Goal: *Be the player with the most points at the end of 10 rounds*

Group Size: *Partners*

Materials: *10 small paper cups, a marker, a tennis ball, recording sheet*

Directions:

1. Before playing the game, prepare the cups by writing the numbers 1–10 on the outside of the cups. Place the cups in a bowling alley formation.
2. Player 1 rolls the tennis ball at the 10 cups. Player 1 uses the cups that fall down to make combinations to 10. On her recording sheet, Player 1 records one tally mark for every combination made.
   If all 10 cups are knocked over on the first try, Player 1 gets a bonus of five tally marks (similar to a strike in bowling), and then it's Player 2's turn. But if there are still cups standing, Player 1 moves to Step 3.
3. Player 1 rolls the ball again, knocks over more cups, and tries to make more combinations of 10. Newly knocked over cups can be combined with cups that have already been knocked over. Player 1 records one tally mark for each combination she makes.
   If all 10 cups are knocked over after this second roll, the player gets a bonus of two tally marks (similar to a spare in bowling).
4. When Player 1's turn is over, the cups are placed back in starting position, and Player 2 takes a turn following the directions in Steps 2 and 3.
5. Players take turns through 10 rounds.

Deal a Double

Goal: *Be the player who has collected the most cards at the end of the game*

Group Size: *Small groups*

Materials: *a deck of cards with all face cards removed* (Ace = 1)

Directions:

1. Sit in a way that allows each player to clearly see each card as it is being turned over.
2. One player turns over a card, and the watching students mentally double that card.
3. The first player to say the card's correct double gets to keep the card.
4. The deck is passed to the next player, and Steps 2 and 3 are repeated.
5. Play continues until all of the cards are gone.

NOTE: If there is any dispute about an answer, the dealer decides who is correct.

Exact-O-Mo!

Exact-O-Mo

Goal: *Be the player with the most points at the end of the game*

Group Size: *Partners*

Materials: *a deck of cards with all face cards removed (Ace = 1)*

Directions:

1. Each player grabs a stack of cards. This does not need to be a complete deck, and it may exceed 52 cards.
2. Players agree on a target number between 20 and 50.
3. One player turns over a card in the center of the playing space. Player 1 then turns over another card, and then uses the two cards to say an addition equation. For example, if the first card was a 5, and the second card was a 7, Player 1 would say, "5 + 7 = 12." Player 2 determines if Player 1 is correct.
4. If the target number has not been reached, Player 2 turns over a card and adds it to Player 1's total. For example, if Player 2 turned over a 3, she would say, "12 + 3 = 15."
5. Players continue taking turns until the target number is reached. If the sum goes higher than the target number, the next player must subtract the flipped card. Once the total dips lower than the target number, players once again add flipped cards. This process continues until a player "hits" the target number exactly. The player who flips over the card that "hits" the target number gets a point.

Once the target number is reached, play starts at 0, and players take turns adding and subtracting to reach the target number again, playing for as long as time allows.

Doubles, Doubles + 1, Other Adding Fun

Doubles	Doubles +1	Other

Goal: *Correctly guess which strategy category will win*

Group Size: *Small group*

Materials: *a deck of cards with all face cards removed (Ace = 1), OR two 6-sided dice (easier version) or two 10-sided dice (more challenging), three-column chart*

Directions:

1. Each player takes a copy of the three-column chart labeled Doubles, Doubles + 1, and Other Adding Fun.
2. Each player makes a prediction about which column will "win"—meaning which strategy will be used the most. Will it be the Doubles strategy, the Doubles + 1, or the Other?
3. Player 1 rolls the dice or turns over two cards, and then determines which addition strategy will best serve them. For example, if the two numbers are 4 and 4, the best strategy would be Doubles, and Player 1 would write "4 + 4 = 8" in the Doubles column on his or her chart. If a 4 and 5 are rolled/turned over, the best strategy would be Doubles + 1 because "4 + 4 = 8 and one more is 9." If neither Doubles nor Doubles + 1 can be used to add the two numbers, then Player 1 would record the number sentence in the column Other Adding Fun.
4. Play continues until each player has taken a predetermined number of turns.
5. Players then total their columns and see if their prediction matched their outcome.

Power Tower

Goal: *Collect as many cups as you can to build a tower*

Group Size: *Individual*

Materials: *small cups labeled with math facts on the outside, answers on the inside, a container to hold the cups*

Directions:

1. Choose a container of cups and take it to your seat. Take the stack of cups out of the container.
2. Take the first cup from the top of the stack. Solve the math problem you see on the cup. Check inside the cup to see if you have the correct answer.
3. If you answered correctly, you get to keep the cup! If you did not answer correctly, return the cup to the bottom of the stack.
4. As you collect cups, build the highest or most interesting tower you can by stacking the cups you earned.

Your goal is to use all of the cups to build your tower!

7+7= 3-2=
1+4= 8-1= 10-3=
8+8= 11+3= 9-4= 6+7=
5

Rock, Paper, Scissors, Sums!

Goal: *Be the player to win two out of three rounds*

Group Size: *Whole group, partners*

Materials: *None—just your hands!*

Directions:

1. Players can find the nearest partner or they can stand in two circles—one inner circle, and one outer circle. Players should stand facing each other and "partner up."
2. To play, the two partners say together, "Rock, paper, scissors, sums!" while tapping their fists into their palms—one tap each for "rock," "paper," and "scissors."
3. When players say "sums," each "throws" a number of fingers.
4. As quickly as they can, both players find the sum of the two numbers shown on their hands. The first player to say the correct sum wins that round.
5. Play continues with the same partner until a player wins two out of three rounds.
6. After three rounds, players in the outer circle rotate over one partner and play again.

Face Off

Goal: *Be the player with the most cards at the end of the game*

Group Size: *Partners*

Materials: *a deck of cards with all face cards removed (Ace = 1)*

Directions:

1. Divide the cards evenly between both players.
2. Both players turn over their top card at the same time.
3. Each player mentally adds the two numbers and shouts out the sum as quickly as possible.
4. The first player to say the correct sum gets to keep both cards.
5. If it is a tie, both players turn over three more cards and try again. The first person to find the correct sum of the last cards turned over gets to keep all of the turned-over cards.
6. Play continues until one player is out of cards.

Target 10 and Target 55

Goal: *Be the first player to reach the target number*

Group Size: *Partners*

Materials: *game boards and counters*

Directions for Target 10:

1. Players take turns placing counters on the board as each tries to reach the target number 10.
2. Each time a player places a counter, that player must say the total of the numbers covered up to that point.
3. The first player to reach 10 exactly wins the game!

Directions for Target 55:

1. Both players agree on a target number between 25 and 55.
2. Players take turns placing counters on the board as each tries to reach the target number.
3. Each time a player places a counter, that player must say the total of the numbers he has covered.
4. The first player to reach the target number exactly wins the game!

Fast 10s

Goal: *Earn the most points by the end of the game*

Group Size: *Partners*

Materials: *a deck of cards with all 10s and face cards removed (Ace = 1)*

Directions:

1. Player 1 shuffles the deck and places nine cards facing up in a 3 x 3 array (3 rows, 3 columns).
2. Player 2 looks for two cards that, when added together, make 10. Player 2 must find this pair of cards in about five seconds to keep the game moving. If he finds a pair, he takes the two cards and sets them in his side pile.
3. Player 2 now turns over two cards to fill in the empty spaces, and it's Player 1's turn to find two cards that make 10.
4. Players should be looking ahead to plan for pairs for when it is their turn.
5. If no two cards make 10, the player who could not make a pair may add a fourth row of three cards and try again.
6. Play continues until there are no cards left.
7. Players total their card point values. The person with the greatest value of cards (not necessarily most matches) is the winner.

Countdown

Goal: *Be the first player to turn over all of the numbers*

Group Size: *Small groups, partners*

Materials: *index cards for the numbers 0–10 (one set per player), a pair of dice, paper and pencil for recording*

Directions:

1. All players lay out their number cards 0–10 in order, face up.
2. The first player rolls the dice and either adds or subtracts to find a sum or difference that is shown on one of the cards.
3. If the roll is between 0–10, the player turns over or crosses off that number. For example, if the sum or difference (whichever operation is being used for that round) of the roll was 3, the player that rolled turns over his or her 3 card.
4. The player who rolled records the number sentence used to get the sum or difference.
5. If the roll is a 5 and a 6, it can only be used as an 11. When an 11 is rolled, the other player(s) must return any of their turned-over numbers back to their number side. The player who rolled is "safe."
6. If the roll is 12, that means the person rolling has to turn over her own cards to their original positions, and the other players are "safe."
7. If no number sentence will work, the player loses his turn, and it is the next player's turn.

Players keep taking turns until there are no cards or numbers left to turn over.

Bonds to 10

Goal: *Make bonds of 10 and then guess the Mystery Card*

Group Size: *Whole class, small groups, partners, individual*

Materials: *a deck of cards with all face cards removed (Ace = 1)*

Directions:

1. Pull one card. Do not look at it. This will be your Mystery Card. Set this card aside.
2. Deal out 11 cards face up.
3. If there are any 10s, cover them with a new card (face up) from the deck because 10 + 0 = 10.
4. Now, look for two cards that are face up and equal 10 when added together. For example, 5 + 5 = 10 or A (1) + 9 = 10. Cover those cards with new cards from the deck. These new cards should also be facing up.
5. Continue to cover 10s with new cards from the deck until the deck is gone.
6. If you are left with a 10 in your deck, set it aside.
7. Look at the piles on the desk. Find two piles whose top cards make 10 when added together. For example, a pile with an 8 on top can be put with a pile with a 2 on top. Continue until only one pile is left.
8. That pile and your Mystery Card should equal 10! Can you guess what your Mystery Card is before flipping it over?

Make Your Own Rekenrek

Materials: *Needlepoint canvas or foam board*

Red and white pony beads (10 of each)

2 Chenille stems

Directions:

1. Place the chenille stems lengthwise on the canvas. Leave space between them.
2. Secure one end of each stem to the back of the canvas.
3. String the pony beads. String 5 white, then 5 red beads on each stem.
4. Secure the open ends of the stems to the back of the canvas.
5. To use the rekenrek, place the white beads on the left. Left will be your start position.

Fast Factors

Goal: *Get through the deck of cards as quickly and accurately as possible*

Group Size: *Partners, individual*

Materials: *a deck of cards with all face cards removed (Ace = 1)*

Directions:

1. Decide what factor(s) you want to work on. Pull one of those cards from the deck. For example, if you are working on your facts that contain a factor of 7, pull a 7 from the deck.
2. Shuffle the remaining cards and place them face down.
3. Turn over a card from the deck and say the math fact using that card and your previously pulled card. For example, if you pulled a 7 and then turned over a 6, the fact you'd say is 7 x 6 = 42. Use a friend, a multiplication chart, or a calculator to check your work.
4. If you are correct, place your card to the side. If incorrect, the card goes to the bottom of the deck to be practiced again as it comes up in the pile.
5. Repeat Steps 3 and 4 until the deck is gone!

7 x 6 = 42

Dividing Cookies

Goal: *Collect the most cookies*

Group Size: *Small group*

Materials: *one die, 15 counters (to represent the "cookies"), six paper plates, recording sheet*

Directions:

1. Set out the 15 counters or "cookies."
2. Player 1 rolls the die and takes the number of plates rolled.
3. Player 1 then divides the "cookies" (the whole) onto the plates (part). Player 1 keeps any cookies that could not divide equally. These are the remaining cookies (the remainder).
4. Slide the cookies from the plates and put them back into the middle of the table. Restack the plates.
5. Player 2 rolls and repeats Steps 2 through 4.
6. After playing several rounds, begin recording the equations on the recording sheet to show what happened during each turn.
   For example:
   15 cookies (whole) divided by 6 plates (part) equals 2 cookies per plate (part) with 3 cookies left over (a remainder of 3). Or 15 ÷ 6 = 2 r3 or 15/6 = 2 r3.
7. Play continues until all cookies have been kept (or "eaten").
8. The player who kept the most cookies wins.

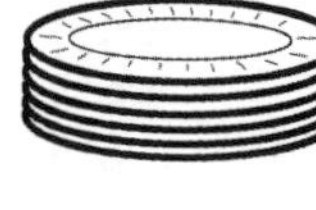

Maze Multiplication

Goal: *Be the first player to get through the maze*

Group Size: *Small group*

Materials: *one or two decks of cards with all face cards removed (Ace = 1); game pieces such as chips, beans, buttons, etc. (one for each player); one die (this can be a standard die with factors 1–6, a modified die with one factor needing practice, or a modified die with factors greater than 6)*

Directions:

1. Use playing cards to create a maze by laying cards, face up, end to end, in any formation you want, such as a spiral, zig zag, a straight line, etc. This is the game board.
2. Place the game pieces on the first card. This is the start position.
3. Player 1 rolls the die and uses the start card number and die roll as the two factors to multiply. For example, if the start card was 3 and the die rolled a 5, then the factors are 3 and 5.
4. Player 1 says the math sentence aloud, including the product, and if correct, moves her game piece forward the number of spaces rolled on the die. If the player is incorrect, the next player begins his turn.
5. Players continue to take turns until the entire maze of cards has been completed by at least one player.

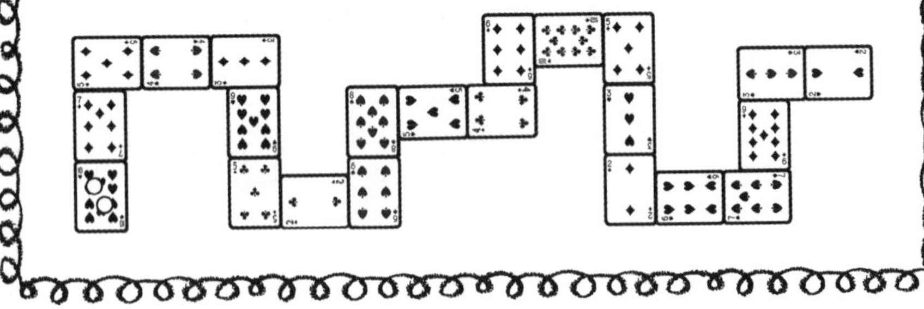

Facts on the Forehead

Goal: *Collect the most cards*

Group Size: *Groups of three*

Materials: *a deck of cards with all face cards removed (Ace = 1)*

Directions:

1. Choose the Product Maker.
2. Divide the deck of cards into two piles; each player who is not the Product Maker gets half of the cards.
3. The Product Maker counts down from 3.
4. At 0, the two players with cards hold their top card (or factor) face out on their forehead. **Note:** Each player cannot see his or her own card. Players can only see the other player's card.
5. The Product Maker says the product of the two factors.
6. Now that the product is known, the players holding cards must determine the factor on their forehead by using the known product and the other visible factor.
7. The first player to say his factor receives both cards.
8. Repeat steps until all factors have been played.

For an easier version, play with two players:

1. Choose a known factor. For example, if a player needs to work on her 5s, 5 will be the known factor for the entire game.
2. One player turns over a card and places it on her forehead.
3. The Product Maker (the other player) says the product.
4. The player holding the card finds her factor by using the known factor of 5 and the product provided.

Doubles	Doubles +1	Other

Cookies

Player	# of Cookies	# of Plates	Equation	# Leftover

Bowling for 10

Partner A: ______________________

1	2	3	4	5

6	7	8	9	10

Total points: ___________

Partner B: ______________________

1	2	3	4	5

6	7	8	9	10

Total points: ___________

Target 10

Directions:

1) *Find a partner to play with.*
2) *The target number is 10.*
3) *Take turns placing markers on the board trying to reach 10.*
4) *Each time a marker is placed, give the current total of the numbers covered.*
5) *The first player to reach the target number exactly wins!!*

1	1	1	1	1
1	1	1	1	1
2	2	2	2	2
2	2	2	2	2
3	3	3	3	3
3	3	3	3	3

Target 55

Directions:

1) *Find a partner to play with.*
2) *Choose a target number between 25 and 55.*
3) *Take turns placing markers on the board trying to reach the target number.*
4) *Each time a marker is placed, give the current total of the numbers covered.*
5) *The first player to reach the target number exactly wins!!*

5	5	5	5	5
4	4	4	4	4
3	3	3	3	3
2	2	2	2	2
1	1	1	1	1

Timely Tens Recording Sheet

Name: ____________________________

Record your number sentences to show the two numbers you rolled and how it looks on the ten-frames.

1. ________ + ________ = ________ + ________ = ________

2. ________ + ________ = ________ + ________ = ________

3. ________ + ________ = ________ + ________ = ________

4. ________ + ________ = ________ + ________ = ________

5. ________ + ________ = ________ + ________ = ________

6. ________ + ________ = ________ + ________ = ________

7. ________ + ________ = ________ + ________ = ________

8. ________ + ________ = ________ + ________ = ________

Addition Journal Reproducible Pages

The following pages could be put together for the students to keep track of their work while they are developing their understanding of addition and subtraction. Some suggestions on how to use the activities are listed below:

Number Bracelet Pictures After the students have made their number bracelets (pg. 19), have them draw what the beads look like in different arrangements. For example, if we are working on the number 5, one bracelet could show 1 bead on the left and 4 beads on the right. Another bracelet could show 2 beads on the left and 3 beads on the right. Have your students draw several different representations of the beads. Encourage them to think of multiple parts as well.

Number Bonds In class use the activity on pg. 36 to demonstrate how to use the part whole relationship to develop understanding of the Commutative Property of Addition. This page in the journal can be a recording to show students understanding from the lesson. For example, if we are working on the number 5, a student would put 5 in the whole and 2 and 3 in the parts. They would record the following equations:

$2 + 3 = 5$; $3 + 2 = 5$; $5 - 2 = 3$; $5 - 3 = 2$

Again, encourage children to show multiple ways to decompose the number.

Personal Number Story After students have shared oral stories of the target number, have them record their own story in their journal. Be sure to encourage them to draw a picture and record their number sentence to match the story.

Connection to Ten Let's say our target number is five. In class pass out a ten frame and five counters to each child. Have students place their counters on the ten frame. Now ask them, "How many more do we need to make 10?" Tell children to show you a different arrangement with the five counters on the ten frame. Ask again, "How many more do we need to make 10?" Repeat this a third time and possibly a fourth time. The idea is for students to identify that it doesn't matter how the counters are arranged, it will still be 5+5=10. In their journals have them show different arrangements of the target number on the ten frame. Underneath the ten frame have students record the equation.

Number Bracelet Pictures

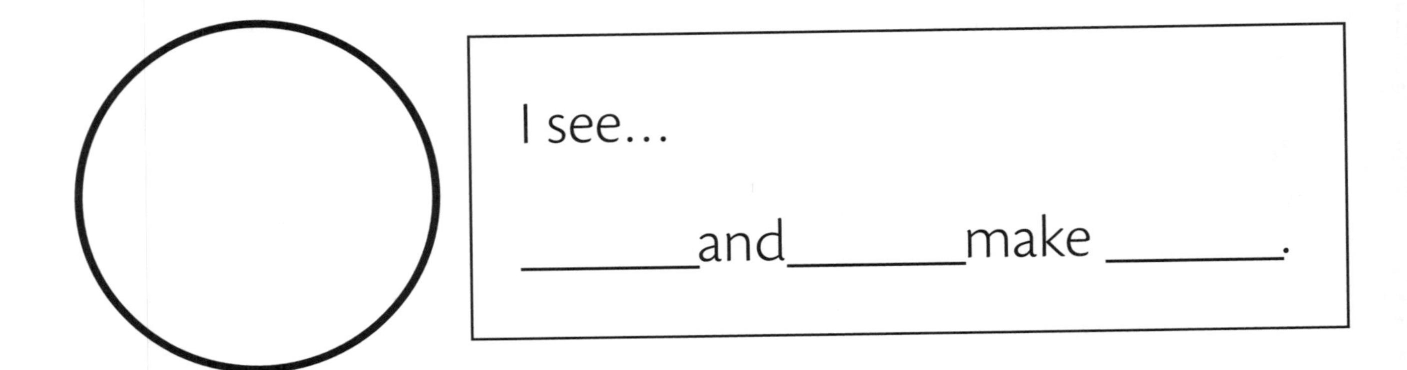

I see...

_______ and _______ make _______.

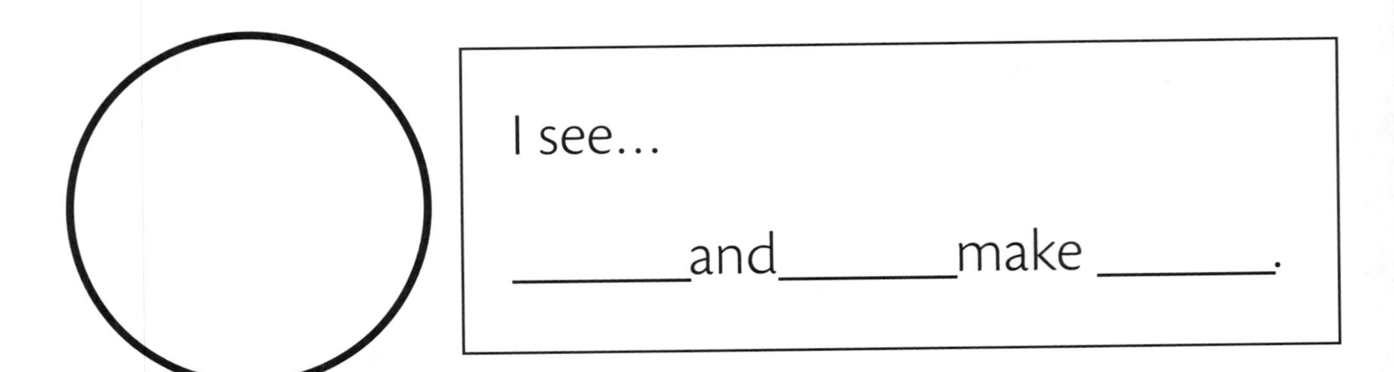

Number Bonds

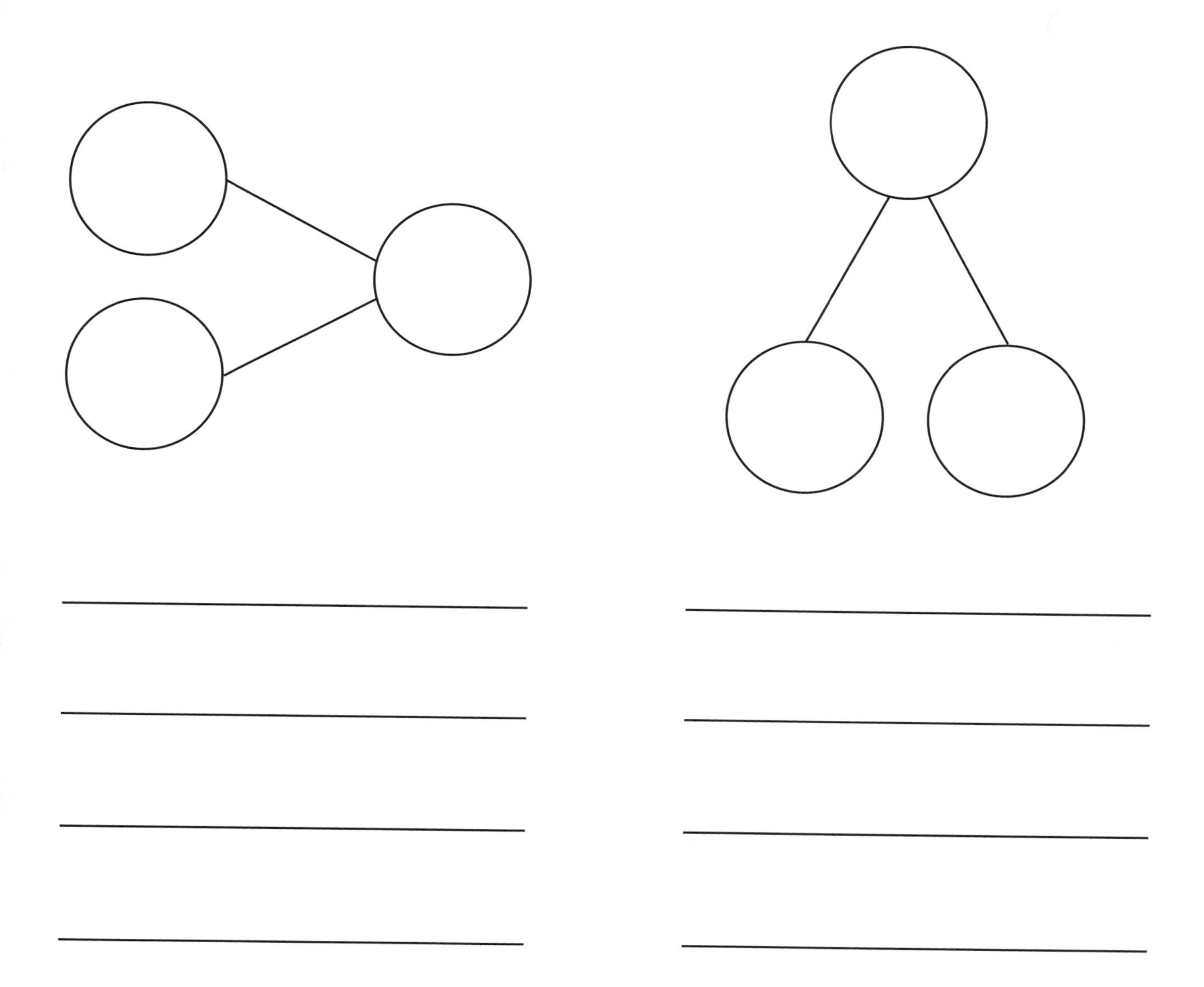

Personal Number Story

My math story of ________:

____

____

____

____

____

Number sentence: ______________________________

Connection to Ten

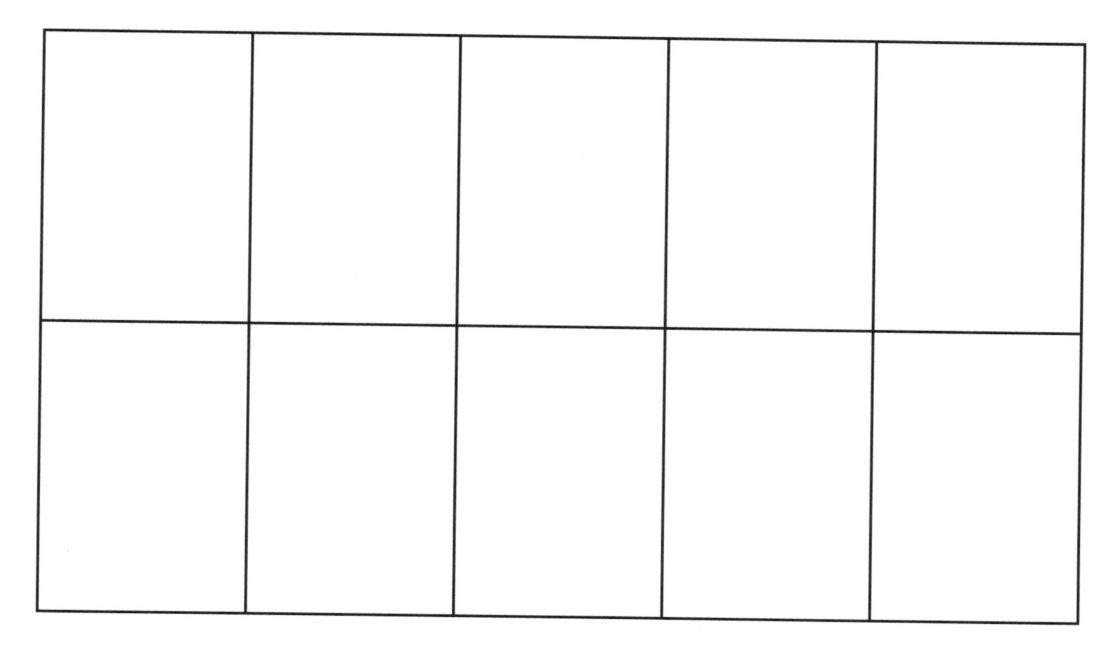

_______ + _______ = _______

10 x 10

Double 10-frame Board

Glossary

abstract (adj): the final stage in the math continuum where students demonstrate an understanding of the process by solving the problem with an algorithm

compose (v): to put a number's parts back together; For example, the number 432 can be composed of 400, 30, and 2, or 200, 200, and 32.

concept of number bonds (n): understanding how numbers "bond" together by composing and decomposing them into their part-to-whole relationship

concrete (adj): using hands-on manipulatives to deliver math instruction conceptually (i.e., teddy bear counters, base-10 blocks, bean sticks, etc.)

Cuisenaire rods (n): hands-on manipulatives that help students learn mathematical basics

decompose (v): to break a number into parts; For example, the number 346 can be broken into 3 hundreds, 4 tens, and 6 ones, or 1 hundred, 1 hundred, 1 hundred, and 46 ones.

fluency (n): the ability to solve a math fact with understanding; to solve with accuracy and efficiency

inverse relationship (n): when two operations are related and work together; in addition, parts are put together to make a whole, such as 3 + 5 = 8; in subtraction, parts are taken away from the whole, such as 8 – 5 = 3; the inverse relationship arises because of the balance between the operations on either side of the equal sign

pictorial (adj): representing numbers, equations, or word problems with pictures or other visual representations (i.e., drawn pictures of items, model drawing, bar models, tape diagrams, strip diagrams, etc.)

rekenreks (n): arithmetic racks made up of rods and beads

schema (n): an organization of concepts and actions

story of a number (n): all of the ways a number can be considered and examined

tape diagram (n): a visual representation that shows the relationship between quantities using rectangles as units.

timed test (n): a short timing done repeatedly to measure speed of fact recall, typically used with addition and subtraction within 20 and/or multiplication and division of facts up to 12 x 12, or up to 144 divided by 12.

Bibliography

Boaler, J. "Fluency Without Fear: Research Evidence on the Best Ways to Learn Math Facts" (youcubed@stanford) w/ help from Cathy Williams, co-founder youcubed, & Amanda Confer Stanford University

---. 2016. ***Mathematical Mindsets***. San Francisco, CA: Josey-Bass Publishers.

---. 2015. ***What's Math Got to Do With It? How Teachers and Parents Can Transform Mathematics Learning and Inspire Success.*** New York: Penguin.

Burns, Marilyn. 2007. ***About Teaching Mathematics: A K-8 Resource Guide.*** (3rd ed.). Sausalito, CA: Math Solutions.

Kuhns, Catherine. 2006. ***Number Wonders***. Peterborough, NH: Crystal Springs Books.

Parrish, S. 2014. ***Number Talks: Helping Children Build Mental Math and Computation Strategies, Grades K 5***, Updated with Common Core Connections. Sausalito, CA: Math Solutions.

Ramirez, G., Gunderson, E., Levine, S., and Beilock, S. 2013. "Math Anxiety, Working Memory and Math Achievement in Early Elementary School." Journal of Cognition and Development.

Sorte-Thomas, Eliza. 2014. ***Math Play: 40 Engaging Games for the Differentiated Classroom***. Peterborough, NH: Crystal Springs Books.

Special contributions of colleagues, teachers, & students
--Ricky Mikelman (Houston, TX)
--Jane Felling (Edmonton, Alberta)
--Kim Burnham (Kalispell, MT)
--Vickie Poston-Buck (Kalispell, MT)
--Brad Nikunen (Kalispell, MT)
--Emily Kappel (Kettering, OH)
--Terri Hueckstaedt (Rock Springs, WY)
--Justin Cline (Kettering, OH)
--Helen Strines (Carmel, IN)
--Vickie Robbins (Kalispell, MT)
--Kerrie More (Kalispell, MT)
--3rd Grade Teachers at Beavertown Elementary School (Kettering, OH)
--3rd Grade Teachers at Libby Public Schools (Libby, MT)
--4th & 5th Grade Teachers at West Valley Public Schools (Kalispell, MT)

161